SPANISH
for Mastery 1
WORKBOOK

Jean-Paul Valette
Rebecca Valette

D.C. HEATH AND COMPANY
Lexington, Massachusetts   Toronto

ILLUSTRATIONS: Mel Dietmeier
COVER DESIGN: Josephine McGrath

CONTENTS

Note to the Student:

Each Unit of your Workbook consists of four parts:

The lesson exercises
which will give you the opportunity to develop your writing skills and put in practice what you have learned in class. Each exercise is coded to correspond with a particular part of the **Estructuras** section in your text. For example:

Exercise A1 is the first exercise relating to part A of the **Estructuras**;

Exercise A2 is the second exercise relating to part A.

The exercises with a V code are vocabulary exercises that correspond to a lesson's vocabulary sections. The code in Unit 1 is slightly different since there are no **Estructuras** sections in that unit. AV1 indicates that the vocabulary covered is from part A of that lesson.

If you encounter a problem with a particular exercise, you can quickly refer back to the corresponding explanations and examples in your text.

A *Rincón cultural*
which contains realia from Hispanic countries, various types of games, and stylistic and cultural exercises.

A section titled *Enrich your vocabulary*
which will help you expand your English vocabulary through Spanish. Your teacher may assign this section for extra credit.

A *Test/Repaso*
which will help you review for the Unit Test.

As you do the various exercises in the Workbook, check that you are spelling the words correctly. Don't forget the accents.

And now, ¡Adelante!

Jean-Paul Valette   *Rebecca M. Valette*

UNIDAD 1
LECCIÓN 1 Presentaciones

1. En el club internacional

It is opening day at the international club. The following young people are meeting for the first time. Complete the dialogs.

José: ¿Cómo te llamas?

Isabel: _____*Me llamo*_____ Isabel. ¿Y tú?

José: _____ José.

Isabel: ¿ _____ de Colombia?

José: No, _____ de México.

Carmen: ¿Cómo _____ ?

Alejandro: _____ Alejandro. ¿Y _____ ?

Carmen: _____ Carmen.

2. Nombres de pila *(First names)*

Here are some popular Spanish first names. Can you guess the equivalent English names?

chicos:

	chicas:	
Alejandro *Alexander*	Ana *Ann*
Andrés _____	Carolina _____
Antonio _____	Clara _____
Carlos _____	Cristina _____
Federico _____	Elena _____
Felipe _____	Emilia _____
Francisco _____	Francisca _____
Jaime _____	Juana _____

José	_____	Julia	_____
Juan	_____	Lucía	_____
Luis	_____	Luisa	_____
Miguel	_____	María	_____
Pedro	_____	Raquel	_____
Ramón	_____	Rosa	_____
Ricardo	_____	Susana	_____
Tomás	_____	Teresa	_____

Of the above boys' names, which ones have a written accent? _____

_____

How many end in **-o**? _____

Of the above girls' names, which ones have a written accent? _____

How many end in **-a**? _____

3. Apellidos (*Last names*)

Read the following names: Juan García   Carmen Montero   Susana González
José Morales   Eva López   Andrea Fernández   Emilia Suárez   José Luis Rivas
Isabel Muñoz   Celia María Castro   Teresa Camacho   Carlos Mendoza

These people are all U.S. citizens of Hispanic origin. Can you think of six other last names of Hispanic origin? (In your school there may be students or teachers with Hispanic names. You could also consult a phone directory or a list of baseball players. Thinking of six Spanish names should not be difficult. After all, there are millions of Americans of Hispanic origin!)

_____   _____   _____

_____   _____   _____

Geografía

Here is a list of 18 U.S. cities that have Spanish names. Match them with the states in which they are located. The states, too, have Spanish names. You may look in an atlas for maps of each state; then find the cities.

Albuquerque / Amarillo / El Paso / Fresno / Laredo / Las Vegas / Los Angeles
Palo Alto / Pensacola / Pueblo / Sacramento / San Antonio / San Diego
San Francisco / San Jose / Santa Ana / Santa Barbara / Santa Fe

1. California: *Los Angeles* _____

2. Colorado: _____

3. Florida: _____

4. Nevada: _____

5. New Mexico: _____

6. Texas: _____

LECCIÓN 2   ¡Hola!

1. Diálogos

Several people meet in the street. Complete their conversations.

Diálogo 1:   Luis y Carmen

Carmen: ¡ _Hola_ , Luis!

Luis: ¡Hola, Carmen! ¿ _____ tal?

Carmen: ¡ _____ mal!

Diálogo 2:   Marisol y José

José: ¡ _____, Marisol! ¿ _____ estás?

Marisol: ¡ _____, gracias! ¿ _____?

José: ¡Regular!

Diálogo 3:   la Sra. de Martínez y la Sra. de Ochoa

Sra. de Martínez: ¡ _____ días, Sra. de Ochoa!

Sra. de Ochoa: ¡ _____, Sra. de Martínez! ¿ _____ está _____?

Sra. de Martínez: Así, así . . .

2. En la calle *(In the street)*

As she goes to and from school, María, who is 14 years old, meets several people. Write how she greets each one of them. Follow the model.

ᔓ   Sra. de Muñoz

ᔓ   Felipe

Buenos días, Sra. de Muñoz.
¿Cómo está Ud.?

Hola, Felipe. ¿Cómo estás?

1.   Sr. Castro   _____

2. Srta. Pérez

_____

_____

3. Carlos

_____

_____

4. Carmen

_____

_____

5. Sra. de Ochoa

_____

_____

6. Manuel

_____

_____

3. Carmen

Carmen meets many people during the day. Look at the times given and say how she's going to greet them. Use the appropriate expression, beginning with **Buenos** or **Buenas**.

➣ 2 p.m.   *¡ Buenas tardes !* _____

1. 11 a.m.   _____

2. 11 p.m.   _____

3. 4 p.m.   _____

4. 9 p.m.   _____

5. 10 a.m.   _____

6. 7 a.m.   _____

LECCIÓN 3   ¿Cuánto es?

AV1.   Números de teléfono

Write down your own phone number and the numbers of three friends or relatives. Then write the numbers in Spanish.

<u>5</u> <u>2</u> <u>7</u> <u>1</u> <u>9</u> <u>4</u> <u>8</u>   *cinco-dos-siete-uno-nueve-cuatro-ocho* _____

— — — — — — — _____

— — — — — — — _____

— — — — — — — _____

AV2.   La cuenta *(The bill)*

Imagine you are a serving person in a Spanish cafeteria. Prepare the bills below by writing out the numbers on the basis of the price list.

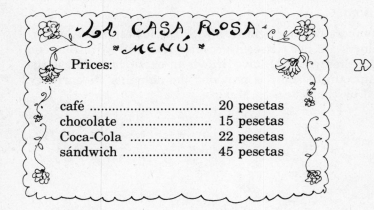

LA CASA ROSA
MENÚ

Prices:

café	20 pesetas
chocolate	15 pesetas
Coca-Cola	22 pesetas
sándwich	45 pesetas

1 café	*veinte pesetas*
2 chocolates	*treinta pesetas*
	cincuenta pesetas

1.

2 cafés	_____
1 chocolate	_____
	_____

2.

1 Coca-Cola	_____
1 sándwich	_____
	_____

3.

2 chocolates	_____
3 Coca-Colas	_____
	_____

4.

2 cafés	_____
2 chocolates	_____
	_____

BV1. En un mercado

María wants to buy a bracelet (**una pulsera**). She and the vendor are bargaining about the price. Each time she offers five pesos more, the vendor offers to sell for five pesos less. Complete the dialog below in which María and the vendor finally agree on a price.

María: Perdón, señor. ¿ _____ cuesta la pulsera?

Vendedor: ¿La pulsera? Ochenta y cinco pesos, señorita.

María: ¡Cincuenta!

Vendedor: *¡ Ochenta !* _____

María: *¡ Cincuenta y...* _____ !

Vendedor: _____

María: _____

Vendedor: _____

María: _____

Vendedor: Bueno . . . ¡pero es un regalo!

El animal misterioso (*The mysterious animal*)

Join the dots corresponding to the numbers below, beginning with the lowest and ending with the highest. (Note that the numbers are not consecutive: often you will skip from one number to the next.) When you are finished you will have drawn an exotic bird that is the national symbol of a Spanish-speaking country and has provided the name for its currency. This bird was also worshiped as a god by the Aztecs in Mexico.

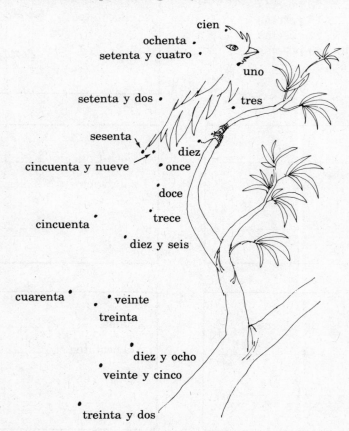

LECCIÓN 4   Una cita

BV1.   Diálogos

Anita's watch is five minutes fast. Whenever she mentions the time, her friend Roberto corrects her. Write the dialogs.

↪ Anita: *Son las dos y cinco.*
   Roberto: *No, son las dos.*

1. Anita: _____
    Roberto: _____

2. Anita: _____
    Roberto: _____

3. Anita: _____
    Roberto: _____

4. Anita: _____
    Roberto: _____

BV2.   El tren

Felipe is taking a train through Spain. Write the time that he arrives at each station.
(**Llega** = *He arrives*)

↪ San Sebastián   **6:00**   Llega a San Sebastián   *a las seis de la mañana.*

1. Burgos   **7:25**   Llega a Burgos _____

2.	Madrid	1:35	_____
			_____
3.	Toledo	3:10	_____
			_____
4.	Córdoba	7:55	_____
5.	Sevilla	10:05	_____
			_____

¿Eres buen intérprete? *(Are you a good interpreter?)*

Imagine that you are accompanying a group of English-speaking tourists to Mexico. Can you guess the meanings of the places where you might be likely to stop? Write the English equivalents.

español	inglés
aeropuerto	*airport*
estación	_____
hotel	_____
restaurante	_____
banco	_____
teatro	_____
cine	_____
hospital	_____
farmacia	_____

Nombre ______________________________ Fecha ____________

LECCIÓN 5 Fechas importantes

V1. La semana *(The week)*

Fit the days of the week into the puzzle. Then write the corresponding dates: Monday is May first.

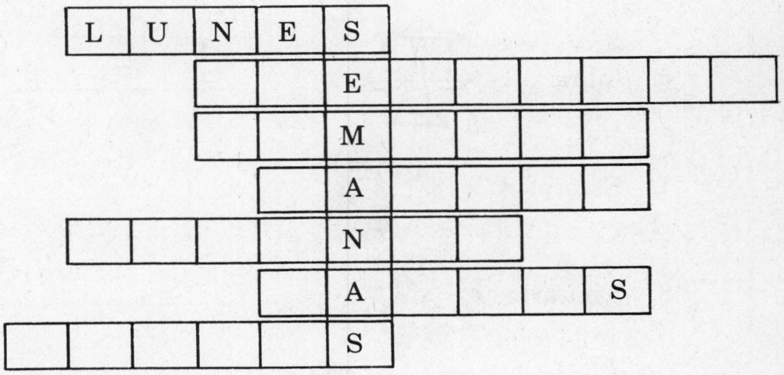

el *primero de mayo*

el *tres de mayo*

1. el ______ *de mayo*
2. el ____________________
3. el ____________________
4. el ____________________
5. el ____________________

V2. Los cumpleaños

Write the dates of the birthdays of six people you know well, beginning with you and members of your family.

José *el veinte y seis de enero*

1. yo *(I)* ____________________
2. mamá ____________________
3. papá ____________________
4. __________ ____________________
5. __________ ____________________
6. __________ ____________________

V3. El horóscopo

Consult the horoscope chart on page 385 of your text and say when each sign begins and ends.

		empieza *(begins):*	termina *(ends):*
Aries		*el 21 de marzo*	*el 20 de abril*
1. Tauro			
2. Géminis			
3. Cáncer			

4. Leo

5. Virgo

6. Libra

7. Escorpión

8. Sagitario

9. Capricornio

10. Acuario

11. Piscis

Medios de transporte

Below are some common means of transportation. Note the words in Spanish. Then group them into three categories:

a) same word in Spanish and English _____

b) slightly different word in Spanish and English _____

_____

c) totally different word in Spanish and English _____

avión

autobús

bicicleta

helicóptero

taxi

coche

moto

tren

LECCIÓN 6   ¿Qué tiempo hace?

BV1.   El tiempo en el lugar donde vivo *(The weather where I live)*

Describe the weather in the city where you live.

Hoy *(today)* hace _____ .

En enero _____ .

Hace _____ grados (temperatura mínima).

En agosto _____ .

Hace _____ (temperatura máxima).

BV2.   Las estaciones del año

A Spanish-speaking friend of yours plans to visit the United States. Describe the type of weather your friend may expect in the following cities.

en Nueva York

En el invierno _____

En la primavera _____

En el verano _____

En el otoño _____

en Miami

En el invierno _____

En la primavera _____

En el verano _____

En el otoño _____

en Chicago

En el invierno _____

En la primavera _____

En el verano _____

En el otoño _____

¿Eres buen intérprete?

The following words have been taken from a directory of professional services. Can you write the English equivalents?

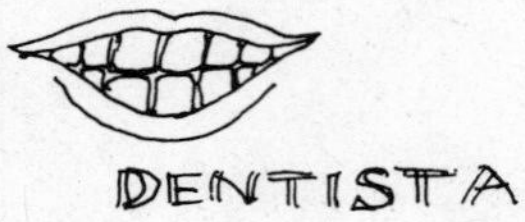

DENTISTA

_____

Mecánico

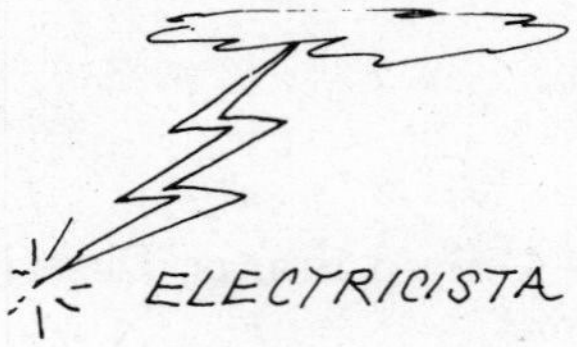

_____

ELECTRICISTA

_____

Actor

_____

fotógrafo

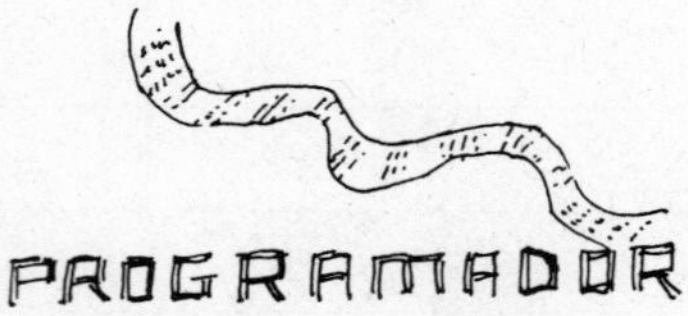

_____

PROGRAMADOR

_____

intérprete

_____

Modelo

_____

pianista

_____

Artista

_____

El rincón cultural *(The cultural corner)*
Direcciones *(Addresses)*

La agenda *(Address book):*

Apellido *(Name)*	Ciudad *(City)*
Arenas, Trinidad	Bogotá, Colombia
Galván, Héctor	Lima, Perú
Jiménez, Graciela	La Paz, Bolivia
García, Mercedes	Caracas, Venezuela
Mantilla, Claudia	Quito, Ecuador
Mendoza, Joaquín	Montevideo, Uruguay
Sandoval, Fabiola	Asunción, Paraguay
Santos, Esteban	Santiago, Chile
Velázquez, Guillermo	Buenos Aires, Argentina

The young people who are listed in the address book have something in common: they each live in the capital city of a Spanish-speaking country. On the map below, write the name of the country and the first name of the person who lives in its capital city.

(Mercedes)
Venezuela

GUYANAS

BRAZIL

(_____)

(_____)

(_____)

(_____)

(_____)

La tarjeta turística *(Tourist card)*

When you register in a hotel in a Spanish-speaking country, you are often asked to fill out a form similar to the one below. Try to fill out this form as completely as possible.

TARJETA TURÍSTICA

Apellido _____

Nombres de pila _____

Nacionalidad _____

Fecha de nacimiento _____

Ocupación _____

Domicilio _____

Teléfono _____

Happy New Year!

How do you say "Happy New Year" in Spanish? Complete the puzzle below with the Spanish months of the year, and discover the answer.

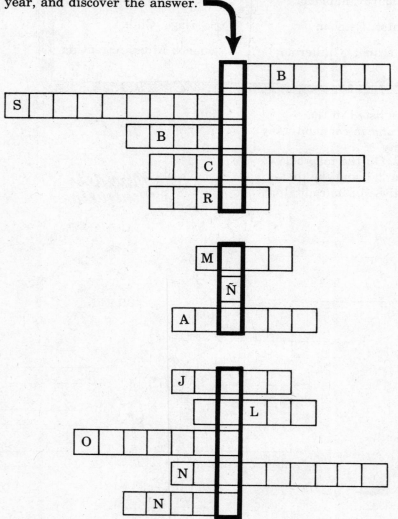

Enrich your vocabulary through Spanish

Learning a foreign language will help you communicate with people of other nationalities. It will also help you improve your knowledge of English. As you have certainly noticed by now, there are many Spanish words which closely resemble English words. Many others are related, although the connection may not immediately be as obvious.

For example, in this chapter you learned the numbers. Maybe you didn't understand them all at first, but you could figure out many of them. Perhaps you remembered that **cuarto** meant "four" because you thought of the English words "quart" (¼ gallon) and "quarter" (¼ dollar).

As you progress through this book, you will note more and more similarities between Spanish and English. These workbook sections, titled "Enrich your vocabulary through Spanish," will help you expand your knowledge of English while making it easier for you to remember the meanings of Spanish words.

English and Spanish: The Latin Connection

Why are there similarities between so many English and Spanish words? The reason is that many words in both languages have the same Latin roots.

To understand the linguistic connection which exists between Spanish and English, we have to go back in history to the second century B.C. At that time, Rome was engaged in a fierce war against Carthage, an ancient city in North Africa which then controlled Sicily and Spain. Carthage lost and had to relinquish Spain to Rome. In order to reach Spain by land, the Roman troops had to go through the southern part of France — Provence — which they also colonized. By the end of the first century A.D., Roman control over the western part of the

Mediterranean was complete. Roman rule brought political unity, law, and economic prosperity. It also brought a common language: Latin.

The Spanish which is spoken today is directly derived from the Latin dialect spoken centuries ago in Spain. Another Latin dialect, spoken in France, became French. Although Romans occupied England for three centuries beginning in 43 A.D., most everyday words of Latin origin entered the spoken English language through French, with the Norman Conquest of England in 1066. This explains why there are many words of Latin origin in the English language. If English and Spanish are related, it is through this common Latin connection.

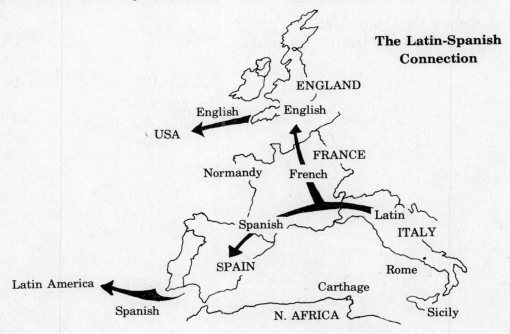

The Latin-Spanish Connection

Most Spanish words relating to weather come directly from Latin. Many English words are related to these same Latin roots. Match the English words in parentheses with their corresponding definitions.

1. **viento** (from the Latin **ventus:** *wind*)

   a. an opening through which air may escape: a _____

   b. a fan for moving air: a _____

   c. to admit fresh air: to _____

                              (ventilate   vent   ventilator)

2. **sol** (from the Latin **sol:** *sun)*

   a. energy from the sun: _____ energy

   b. the longest day of the year, when the sun is highest in the sky: the summer

   _____

   c. a very sunny room or gallery: a _____

                              (solar   solarium   solstice)

3. **calor** (from the Latin **calor:** *heat)*

   a. an apparatus for measuring heat: a _____

   b. the amount of heat needed to raise the temperature of one gram of water by 1° centigrade: a _____

   c. name of a stove which generates heat: a _____ range

                              (caloric   calorie   calorimeter)

4. **frío** (from the Latin **frigidus:** *cold*)

   a. very cold water: _____ water

   b. to keep foods cold: to _____ foods

   c. an appliance which keeps things cold: a _____

                              (frigid   refrigerate   refrigerator)

TEST / REPASO Unidad 1

Test 1 La lotería *(Lottery)*   The following numbers have been drawn at a lottery. Write the numerals that correspond to the written numbers.

⋈	dos	2
1.	ciento	_____
2.	quince	_____
3.	treinta	_____
4.	setenta y cuatro	_____
5.	noventa y nueve	_____
6.	diez y nueve	_____
7.	ochenta y dos	_____
8.	sesenta	_____

Test 2 Antes y después *(Before and after)*   Write down the numbers, days, months, seasons or dates which come before and after those in the middle column.

	Antes			**Después**
⋈	*uno*	dos		*tres*
1.	_____	seis	_____	
2.	_____	nueve	_____	
3.	_____	doce	_____	
4.	_____	quince	_____	
5.	_____	veinte	_____	
6.	_____	lunes	_____	
7.	_____	jueves	_____	

8. _____ | febrero | _____
9. _____ | mayo | _____
10. _____ | agosto | _____
11. _____ | invierno | _____
12. _____ | el cinco de | _____
   _____ | octubre | _____
13. _____ | el dos de | _____
   _____ | diciembre | _____

Test 3   En el aeropuerto   Felipe does not need to look at his watch to know the time. He can tell, by looking at the arrival schedule and listening to the announcement, which plane is landing. Use his method and tell the time according to the model. (Nota: **El avión de París llega** means *The plane from Paris is arriving.)*

LLEGADAS	
París	2:00
Roma	1:00
Madrid	3:10
Nueva York	4:15
Los Ángeles	5:30
Chicago	6:45
Buenos Aires	9:40

➭ El avión de París llega. *¡Son las dos!*

1. El avión de Roma llega. _____

2. El avión de Madrid llega. _____

3. El avión de Nueva York llega. _____

4. El avión de Los Ángeles llega. _____

5. El avión de Chicago llega. _____

6. El avión de Buenos Aires llega. _____

Test 4   El mapa del tiempo *(The weather map)*   Describe the weather in the cities below on the basis of the illustrations.

➭ En Buenos Aires, *hace sol (hace buen tiempo).*

1. En Bogotá _____

2. En Madrid _____

3. En Santiago _____

4. En San Juan _____

5. En Los Ángeles _____

6. En Chicago _____

Test 5   Un encuentro *(A meeting)*   Imagine that you are meeting Teresa, a girl from Bolivia. Have a conversation with her, writing out your replies to what she says.

1. Teresa: ¡Buenos días!

   Tú: _____

2. Teresa: ¿Cómo te llamas?

   Tú: _____

3. Teresa: ¿Eres de México?

   Tú: ¡No! _____

4. Teresa: ¿Cómo estás?

   Tú: _____

5. Teresa: ¡Hasta luego!

   Tú: _____

Test 6   Intérprete   Imagine that you are accompanying a tourist bus to Mexico. People ask you how to say the following things in Spanish. Write out your answers.

1. *What time is it?*   _____

2. *What is today's date?*   _____

3. *How is the weather?*   _____

4. *Please . . .*   _____

5. *Thank you very much.*   _____

6. *You're welcome.*   _____

Test 7 ¿Sí o no?   Indicate whether the information contained in the statements below is true or false by circling **sí** or **no**.

sí   no   1. All Hispanic people live in Spain.

sí   no   2. Today over 200 million people around the world speak Spanish.

sí   no   3. Spanish is spoken in the countries of Central America.

sí   no   4. Hispanic students tend to be more formal with their teachers than American students are.

sí   no   5. Hispanic teenagers are reserved and shy.

sí   no   6. If you are invited to dinner in an Hispanic country it is essential that you arrive on time.

sí   no   7. The **quetzal** and the **bolívar** are monetary units.

sí   no   8. The **peso** is used in several Hispanic countries.

sí   no   9. In Hispanic countries, one's birthday is always **"el día del santo."**

sí   no   10. Birthdays are often the occasion for a big family celebration in Hispanic countries.

sí   no   11. In Argentina and Chile, Christmas comes in summer.

sí   no   12. The metric system is used in Spain and Latin America.

UNIDAD 2

LECCIÓN 1   En San Antonio y en Nueva York

B1.   Presentaciones *(Introductions)*

The following people are introducing themselves. Write what they say.

Nombre: Ana María
Apellido: López
Idiomas: hablar español
Ocupación: estudiar
    inglés
Intereses: cantar, tocar el
    piano

Me llamo María López.
Hablo español.

Nombre: Antonio
Apellido: Ramos
Idiomas: hablar español,
    francés e inglés
Ocupación: estudiar
    arquitectura
Intereses: tocar la
    guitarra, escuchar
    música

Nombre: Juan Carlos
Apellido: Suárez
Idiomas: hablar español e
    inglés
Ocupación: trabajar en
    un laboratorio
Intereses: escuchar
    música popular,
    cantar

C1.   ¿Y tú?

Carlos Aguirre will tell you what he does. Write whether or not you do the same things.

Carlos:

▷ Hablo español. ¿Y tú?

1. Hablo francés. ¿Y tú?

2. Estudio italiano. ¿Y tú?

3. Trabajo mucho. ¿Y tú?

4. Trabajo en Puerto Rico. ¿Y tú?

5. Toco la guitarra. ¿Y tú?

6. Canto muy bien. ¿Y tú?

Tú:

Yo también hablo español.
(Yo no hablo español.)

C2. ¡Qué lástima!

Luis speaks about what he does and then about what he does not do. Write what he says. First use the verb in the picture in the affirmative, and then in the negative with the second cue.

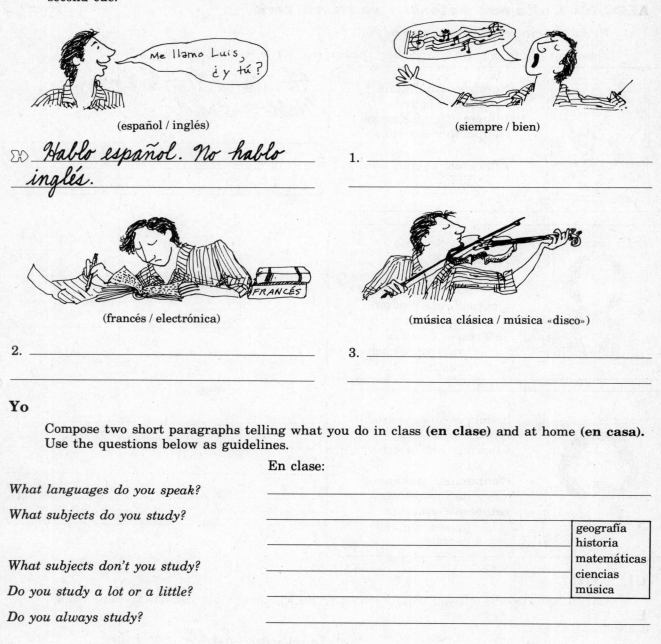

(español / inglés)

(siempre / bien)

> *Hablo español. No hablo inglés.*

1. _____

(francés / electrónica)

(música clásica / música «disco»)

2. _____

3. _____

Yo

Compose two short paragraphs telling what you do in class (**en clase**) and at home (**en casa**). Use the questions below as guidelines.

En clase:

What languages do you speak?

_____

What subjects do you study?

_____

_____

| geografía |
| historia |
| matemáticas |
| ciencias |
| música |

What subjects don't you study?

_____

Do you study a lot or a little?

_____

Do you always study?

_____

En casa:

What languages do you speak?

_____

Do you work?

_____

Do you study (a lot or a little)?

_____

Do you sing (a lot? well?)?

_____

What type of music do you listen to?

_____

| música clásica |
| música popular |
| jazz |

LECCIÓN 2   En el suroeste

A1.   Las ocupaciones

Describe what the following people are doing and what they are not doing. Use the verbs in parentheses.

(estudiar / nadar / mirar la televisión)

⊠ Elena *no estudia. No nada. Elena mira la televisión.*

(viajar / ganar mucho dinero / escuchar la radio)

1. El Sr. Montero _____

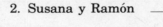

(bailar / escuchar música / trabajar)

2. Susana y Ramón _____

(trabajar mucho / ganar mucho dinero / estudiar)

3. Rubén y Pedro _____

B1.   Críticas

Felipe has a high opinion of himself and a low opinion of others. Complete the dialogs below between Felipe and his friend Susana. Use the verbs suggested by the illustrations.

⊠

Felipe: *Nado* bien.

Susana: ¿Y Ramón? ¿*Nada bien él* ?

Felipe: ¿ *Él* ? ¡No! *No nada bien.*

1.

Felipe: _____ mucho.

Susana: ¿Y Carmen? ¿_____?

Felipe: ¿ *Ella?* ¡No! _____

2.

Felipe: _____ bien.

Susana: ¿Y Alberto y Clara? ¿_____?

Felipe: ¿_____? ¡No! _____

3.

Felipe: _____ bien.

Susana: ¿Y Luis y Roberto? ¿_____?

Felipe: ¿_____? ¡No! _____

B2. Preguntas

Write three questions about the people in each of the pictures below.

el Sr. Ortiz   la Sra. de Ortiz

¿Viaja mucho el Sr. Ortiz?
¿Viaja también la Sra.
de Ortiz? ¿Visitan Nueva
York el Sr. y la Sra. de
Ortiz?

Isabel   Felipe

1.   Ramón   Luisa

_____

_____

_____

_____

2.

_____

_____

_____

_____

_____

_____

Mi familia

Describe what you and members of your family do during vacations.

	yo:	mi hermana (my sister):	mis padres (my parents):
Do you swim?	Nado un poco.	Nada muy bien.	No nadan.
Do you travel?			
Do you watch TV?			
Do you dance?			
Do you work?			

LECCIÓN 3   En Los Ángeles

A1.   Un sondeo de opinión *(An opinion poll)*

Imagine that you are conducting an opinion poll to find out what people do on weekends. Ask each of the following people questions based on the pictures.

Carlos (a friend)

la Sra. de Muñoz (your Spanish teacher)

¿ Miras la televisión?
¿ Mira Ud. la televisión?

1.   Bárbara (your cousin) 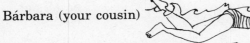 _____

2.   el Sr. Smith (your neighbor) 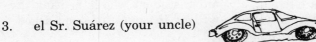 _____

3.   el Sr. Suárez (your uncle)  _____

4.   Roberto (a classmate) _____

B1.   Unos planes de verano

Everyone has different summer plans. To find out what they are, complete the sentences below with the correct forms of **esperar.**

1.   Carlos _____ viajar.

2.   El Sr. Molina _____ visitar México.

3.   Tú _____ ganar dinero.

4.   Yo _____ visitar España.

5.   Ud. _____ trabajar en un hospital.

6.   Ramón y Elena _____ trabajar.

7.   Uds. _____ ganar mucho dinero.

8.   Luisa _____ trabajar en un laboratorio.

C1.   La curiosidad

Tomás is looking at Ramón's photos. He wants to know who the people in each picture are and where each photo was taken. Complete his questions, using **quién** or **quiénes** and the corresponding verb forms.

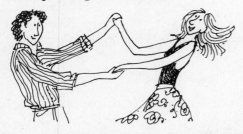

Tomás: *¿ Quiénes bailan ?*

Ramón: Carlos y Elena.

Tomás: *¿ Dónde bailan ellos?*

Ramón: *Bailan* en un hotel.

1.   Tomás: _____

Ramón: Pedro, Paco y Roberto.

Tomás: _____

Ramón: _____ en un restaurante.

2. Tomás: _____

   Ramón: Inés.

   Tomás: _____

   Ramón: _____ en un café.

3. Tomás: _____

   Ramón: Anita y Pedro.

   Tomás: _____

   Ramón: _____ en Miami.

C2. Una entrevista

Imagine that you have just interviewed Dorita Estrada, a Spanish student who is visiting the United States. As you read over the notes you took, you are writing the questions you asked. The words in italics represent the information you requested.

> Tú: *¿Qué estudias, Dorita?* _____

Dorita: Estudio *fotografía*.

1. Tú: ¿ _____ ?

   Dorita: Estudio *en el Instituto Técnico Internacional*.

2. Tú: ¿ _____ ?

   Dorita: Estudio fotografía *porque deseo ser periodista (journalist)*.

3. Tú: ¿ _____ ?

   Dorita: Viajo *con Elena*.

4. Tú: ¿ _____ ?

   Dorita: Trabajo *en un laboratorio*.

5. Tú: ¿ _____ ?

   Dorita: Viajo *durante (during) las vacaciones*.

Una carta (A letter)

Imagine that you have received the name of a Spanish pen pal. Write him a short letter in which you ask him about himself.

Querido Miguel:

Give your name. _____

Ask Miguel if he works, _____

  where he works, _____

  what he is studying, _____

  if he speaks English, and _____

  why he studies English. _____

LECCIÓN 4   En Miami

B1.   Diálogos

Complete the conversations below, using the appropriate forms of the verb given in parentheses.

Diálogo 1.   Antonio y Rafaela

Antonio: ¿Con quién _____*estudias*_____ tú, Rafaela?

Rafaela: _____ con Inés.

Antonio: ¿ _____ Uds. mucho?

Rafaela: ¡Sí y no! Yo _____ mucho, pero Inés . . . ¡ella no

_____ mucho!

(estudiar)

Diálogo 2.   Andrés, Luisa y Paco

Andrés: ¡Hola, Luisa! ¡Hola, Paco!

¿Dónde _____ Uds. ahora?

Luisa: Yo _____ en un hotel.

Andrés: Y tú, Paco, ¿dónde _____?

Paco: _____ en un restaurante.

Andrés: Uds. _____ mucho, ¿verdad?

(trabajar)   Paco: ¡Claro! ¡Nosotros _____ siempre!

Diálogo 3.   El Sr. Vargas y la Sra. de Smith

Sr. V.: Sra. de Smith, ¿ _____ Ud. español?

Sra. de S.: ¡Sí! _____ un poco.

Sr. V.: Y el Sr. Smith, ¿ _____ español también?

Sra. de S.: Él, no. No _____ español.

Sr. V.: ¿ _____ Uds. francés?

(hablar)   Sra. de S.: ¿Nosotros? No, no _____ francés.

Diálogo 4.   José y Antonia

José: Carmen y Pilar _____ muy bien, ¿verdad?

Antonia: ¡Sí, _____ bien!

José: ¿Y tú? ¿ _____ bien también?

Antonia: ¿Yo? . . . ¡No! ¡No me gusta _____!

¡ _____ muy mal!

(nadar)   José: ¡Qué lástima!

C1. Las preferencias personales

Say whether or not you like to do the following things. Then say how often or how well you do (or don't do) them. Use the expressions in parentheses.

✍ nadar *(No) me gusta nadar. (No) nado bien.* (bien)

1. cantar _____ (bien)

2. bailar _____ (bien)

3. ganar dinero _____ (mucho)

4. viajar _____ (mucho)

5. estudiar _____ (siempre)

6. hablar español _____ (bien)

7. hablar inglés _____ (siempre)

8. escuchar la radio _____ (ahora)

D1. La reciprocidad

When we do something for or with people, the situation is often reciprocal. Say this for each of the situations below. Write two sentences according to the model, using pronouns instead of names.

✍ Yo trabajo para Carlos. *Yo trabajo para él.*
Él trabaja para mí.

1. Tú trabajas para Elena. _____

   _____

2. Ramón trabaja con Roberto y Andrés. _____

   _____

3. Isabel y Luisa trabajan para el Sr. Morales. _____

   _____

4. Yo trabajo con Emilia. _____

   _____

5. Tú trabajas con Luis. _____

El rincón cultural

La geografía norteamericana

Although you can probably recognize many names of Spanish origin on a map of the United States, you may wonder what they mean. Here are the *dictionary meanings* of some of these place names.

Arizona:	cities	Casa Grande	big house
		Mesa	table (plateau)
California:	mountains	Sierra Nevada	snow-covered mountains
	cities	Los Angeles	the angels
		Los Gatos	the cats
		Palo Alto	tall stick (tall tree)
		Santa Cruz	Holy Cross
Colorado:	national park	Mesa Verde	green table (green plateau)
	city	Pueblo	village
Florida:	cities	Boca Raton	mouse mouth
		Boca Grande	big mouth
Nevada:	city	Las Vegas	the plains
New Mexico:	mountains	Sierra Blanca	white mountains
	cities	Las Cruces	the crosses
		Los Alamos	the poplars
		Santa Fe	Holy Faith
Texas:	river	El Río Grande del Norte	the big river of the north
	cities	Amarillo	yellow
		El Paso	the pass(age)

Now complete the crossword puzzle below with the place names suggested by the illustrated cues.

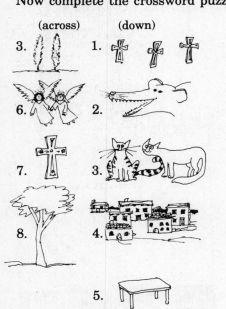

Anuncios y actividades (Ads and activities)

By now you know that there are many words which have similar meanings in English and Spanish. It is sometimes easy to guess the general meaning of a sentence or an expression even if you do not know every word. Look at the advertisements below. Each one illustrates a different activity. Below each one, write the name of the appropriate activity, choosing among the following: **bailar** / **mirar la televisión** / **escuchar música** / **estudiar** / **viajar** / **tocar la guitarra** / **ganar dinero.**

1. _____

2. _____

COLEGIO NUEVA YORK
BILINGÜE INGLES APROBADO
Prekinder, kinder, primaria, bachillerato
Buses a toda la ciudad.
MATRICULAS: Calle 55 No. 10-81, Piso 3o.
INSTALACIONES: Transversal 71 No. 184-80,
Tercer Puente
SOLICITE PROSPECTOS: Teléfono: 2564351.

3. _____

4. _____

5. _____

LOTERIA
DE PUERTO RICO

Primero
23,975

Segundo
0415

Tercero
42.443

6. _____

7. _____

Enrich your vocabulary through Spanish   the Latin connection

Most of the Spanish verbs you have learned in this unit come directly from Latin. Many English words are related to these same Latin roots. Match the English words in parentheses with their corresponding definitions.

1. **bailar** (from the Latin **ballare:** *to dance*)

    a.   a formal party where people dance: a _____

    b.   a room where a formal dance is held: a _____

    c.   an artistic form of dancing: a _____

    d.   a person who performs these artistic dances: a _____
          (ball ballerina ballet ballroom)

2. **cantar** (from the Latin **cantare:** *to sing*)

    a.   Bach wrote many of these choir pieces: _____

    b.   In a Jewish service or ceremony, the person who sings:

          a _____

    c.   a melody in which a number of words are sung on one note:

          a _____
          (cantatas cantor chant)

3. **mirar** (from the Latin **mirare:** *to look at*)

    a.   an object used to look at one's reflection: a _____

    b.   an optical illusion; something that is not what it looks like:

          a _____
          (mirage mirror)

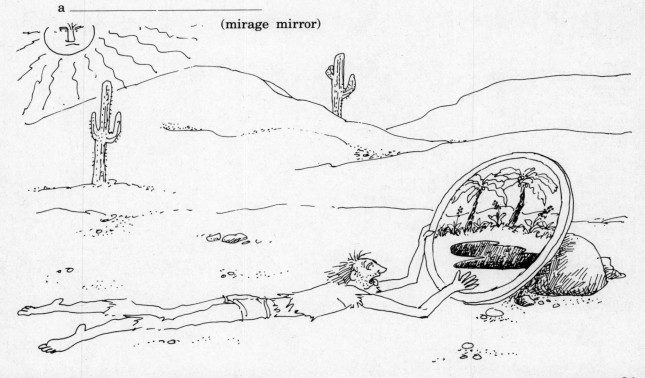

4. **esperar** (from the Latin **sperare:** *to hope*)

a. an artificial language whose name means "one who hopes" (the inventor thought it should be the international language): _____

b. to lose hope: to _____

c. when a situation is hopeless, it is: _____

d. the condition of being without hope: _____
      (despair   desperate   desperation   Esperanto)

5. **necesitar** (from the Latin **necessitas:** *need*)

a. something you need: a _____

b. something which is not needed: an _____ thing

c. a person in need of money: a _____ person

d. to make something needed or necessary: to _____
      (necessitate   necessitous   necessity   unnecessary)

TEST / REPASO   Unidad 2

ESTRUCTURA

Test 1 ¿Tenis?   Ricardo is organizing a tennis tournament and wants to know whether the following people are participating. Complete his questions by using the appropriate pronouns.

⊃⊃ Felipe   ¿Y ___*él*___ ?

1. Teresa   ¿Y _____ ?

2. Carmen and Susana   ¿Y _____ ?

3. María and Luis   ¿Y _____ ?

4. Roberto and Pablo   ¿Y _____ ?

5. you (my best friend)   ¿Y _____ ?

6. you (Srta. Muñoz)   ¿Y _____ ?

7. you (Paco and Alberto)   ¿Y _____ ?

8. you (Mr. and Mrs. Martí)   ¿Y _____ ?

Test 2   En San Carlos de Bariloche   Bariloche is a famous ski resort in Argentina. Say how well the following people are skiing, using the appropriate forms of **esquiar** (a regular **–ar** verb having an accent on the **i** in all forms except for **nosotros**).

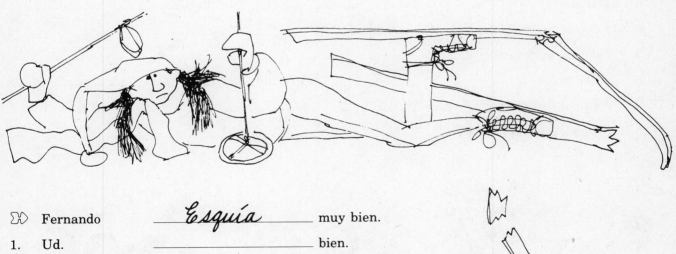
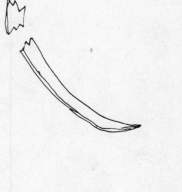

⊃⊃ Fernando   ___*Esquía*___ muy bien.

1. Ud.   _____ bien.

2. Clara   _____ un poco.

3. Ramón y Pedro _____ mal.

4. nosotros   _____ mucho.

5. tú   _____ muy mal.

6. Sra. de Santos _____ bien.

7. yo   _____ muy bien.

8. Carlos y yo   _____ bien.

Test 3   En la fiesta internacional   Pedro is hosting an international party. He asks his friend María whether certain people speak certain languages. Complete the dialog by writing out Pedro's questions and María's answers, using the appropriate forms of **hablar** in the affirmative or negative.

⮕   Pedro: ¿ *Habla inglés Manuel* ?

María: No, Manuel *no habla* inglés.

1.   Pedro: ¿ _____ ?

María: No, Enrique _____ francés.

2.   Pedro: ¿ _____ ?

María: Sí, Adela y Camila _____ italiano.

3.   Pedro: ¿ _____ ?

María: ¡Yo, no! _____ portugués.

Test 4   Intérprete   Imagine that you are an interpreter at an international youth congress in Madrid. Tell an American visitor how to say the following in Spanish. Write out your answers.

1.   *Maybe.*   _____

2.   *Of course.*   _____

3.   *Of course not.*   _____

4.   *I can't.*   _____

5.   *Too bad!*   _____

6.   *I do not speak Spanish.*   _____

7.   *I do not work here.*   _____

8.   *I like to travel.*   _____

9.   *I do not like to speak French.*   _____

10.   *I do not wish to visit Paris.*   _____

Test 5 La reciprocidad   "Reciprocity" means that when you do something for or with someone, that person does the same thing for or with you. Explain this reciprocity by switching around the pronouns in italics and rewriting the sentences according to the model. Make the necessary changes.

🐦 *Yo* trabajo para *ella.*   *Ella trabaja para mí.* _____

1. *Tú* trabajas para *nosotros.* _____

2. *Él* habla de *Ud.* _____

3. *Ella* viaja con *Uds.* _____

4. *Yo* estudio con *él.* _____

5. *Tú* visitas París con *ellos.* _____

VOCABULARIO

Test 6 Actividades   Describe what the following people are doing by completing each sentence with an **–ar** verb which would make sense.

1. El Sr. García _____ para una compañía internacional.

2. Inés _____ en el Océano Atlántico.

3. Raúl _____ la televisión.

4. Carlos _____ la guitarra muy bien.

5. Isabel _____ matemáticas.

6. Manuela _____ la radio.

7. Marisela _____ en el coro de la escuela *(school choir).*

8. La Sra. de Rodríguez _____ mucho dinero.

Test 7 Una conversación   Felipe taped his conversation with Elena. When he played it back, he noticed that some of the interrogative expressions were hard to understand. Read Elena's answers below carefully to see what information they contain. Then fill in the corresponding interrogative expressions in the questions.

Felipe:		Elena:
🐦 ¿ *Quién* _____ es?		¡Es Elena!
1. ¿ _____ estás?		Muy bien, gracias.
2. ¿ _____ trabajas?		Trabajo en Nueva York.
3. ¿ _____ estudias?		Estudio física e inglés.
4. ¿ _____ estudias inglés?		Porque deseo ser intérprete.
5. ¿ _____ es?		Es la profesora.
6. ¿ _____ son?		Son Rafael y Marisa.

CULTURA

Test 8 ¿Sí o no?   Indicate whether the information in the statements below is true or false by circling **sí** or **no**.

sí no   1. Many U.S. cities have Spanish names.

sí no   2. Words like "guitar" and "mosquito" are of Spanish origin.

sí no   3. Spanish is a language spoken by many American citizens.

sí no   4. Spanish is the fourth most commonly spoken language in this country after English, French and German.

sí no   5. The first Spanish explorers to reach the United States landed in San Francisco.

sí no   6. After Plymouth (Massachusetts), Saint Augustine (Florida) is the oldest permanent city of European origin in the United States.

sí no   7. Sacramento (California) is the oldest U.S. seat of government.

sí no   8. Most Spanish speakers living in the United States come from Spain.

sí no   9. Many Mexican-Americans can trace their ancestry to the Indians who lived in North America before the Spanish expeditions.

sí no   10. The Mexican-Americans are the largest group of Spanish speakers in the United States.

sí no   11. Today, one of the main goals of the Puerto Ricans is to become American citizens.

sí no   12. Most of the Spanish speakers who live in New York City come from Cuba.

sí no   13. New York City is one of the largest Spanish-speaking cities in the world.

UNIDAD 3

LECCIÓN 1   En el café

B1. **¿Qué hacen?** *(What are they doing?)*

Describe what the people in each illustration are doing. Follow the model.

⟫ (en la clase)

Hay *una maestra* , *un chico*
y *una chica* .
La maestra habla. El chico
escucha. La chica escucha
también.

1. (en la calle: *in the street*)

Hay _____ y _____ .

_____

_____

2. (en la fiesta)

Hay _____ y _____ .

_____

_____

3. (en el parque)

Hay _____ ,

y _____ .

_____

_____

_____

C1. Los viajeros *(The travelers)*

The following Spanish-speaking people are traveling. Say where they are from and what they are doing. Fill in the first blank with the appropriate form of **ser**, and the second blank with the appropriate form of the verb in parentheses.

∑) El Sr. Cataldo ___*es*___ de Puerto Rico. Ahora ___*viaja*___ a México. (viajar)

1. Inés _____ de Chile. Ahora _____ en Nueva York. (estudiar)

2. Roberto y José _____ de México. Ahora _____ en París. (estudiar)

3. Tú _____ de Guatemala. Ahora _____ en Roma. (trabajar)

4. Nosotros _____ del Uruguay. Ahora _____ en Miami. (trabajar)

5. Ud. _____ de España. Ahora _____ a San Francisco. (viajar)

6. Yo _____ de Bolivia. Ahora _____ a El Paso. (viajar)

7. Marisa _____ de Texas. Ahora _____ en Italia. (trabajar)

8. Uds. _____ de California. Ahora _____ en Chile. (estudiar)

¿Eres buen(a) detective?

Nine people are waiting for a bus. Here are their professions: **doctora / fotógrafo / detective / actor / actriz / guitarrista / estudiante / artista / estudiante.**
Identify each one, writing two sentences according to the model.

∑) Paco 1. Silvia 2. Roberto 3. Inés 4. Carmen 5. José 6. Luis 7. María 8. Antonio

∑) *Hay un guitarrista.*   *El guitarrista es Paco.*

1. _____   _____

2. _____   _____

3. _____   _____

4. _____   _____

5. _____   _____

6. _____   _____

7. _____   _____

8. _____   _____

Nombre ______________________ Fecha ____________

LECCIÓN 2 Los amigos ideales

B1. Es obvio, ¿no? *(It's obvious, isn't it?)*

Match each adjective in column A with its opposite in column B and then use the adjectives to describe one of the people below. Be sure to make the proper noun-adjective agreement.

A		B	
bajo	divertido	aburrido	malo
guapo	antipático	inteligente	moreno
delgado	interesante	serio	feo
rubio	bueno	gordo	alto
tonto		simpático	

Maria es una amiga divertida. No es seria, ¿verdad?

1. Roberto es un chico ______. ______
2. Enrique es un alumno ______. ______
3. Isabel es una muchacha ______. ______
4. La Sra. de Valdez es una profesora ______. ______
5. El Sr. Ortiz es un hombre ______. ______
6. La Sra. de Llosa es una señora ______. ______
7. Paco es un amigo ______. ______
8. Ana María es una estudiante ______. ______

B2. Los retratos *(Portraits)*

Imagine that your school has an exchange program with a school in Colombia, and that four Colombian students are spending the year at your school. Describe each of them to your Spanish pen pal. Use at least three adjectives for each person, in affirmative and negative sentences. End your description by saying whether or not you like to talk with that person.

Marina

Emilio

Marina es bastante delgada. Es muy rubia. No es muy alta. Es guapa y simpática. Me gusta hablar con ella.

1. ______

Beatriz

Pedro

2. _____

_____

_____

_____

3. _____

_____

_____

_____

Críticas

Describe each of the following persons, mentioning their good and bad points.

Woody Allen _____

_____

_____

Elizabeth Taylor _____

_____

_____

El presidente de los Estados Unidos _____

_____

_____

King Kong _____

_____

_____

Carlitos (Charlie Brown) _____

_____

_____

Yo _____

_____

_____

LECCIÓN 3 En la fiesta

B1. ¿Qué tienen?

The following people are carrying objects appropriate to their professions. Identify each one, using the appropriate form of **ser.** Then say which of the following objects each is carrying, using the appropriate form of **tener: cámaras / libros / una guitarra / una raqueta / un clarinete / una grabadora / un estetoscopio** (*stethoscope*).

➤ Isabel ___*es*___ reportera. *Tiene una grabadora.*

1. Nosotros _____ estudiantes. _____

2. Yo _____ campeón de tenis. _____

3. Andrés _____ clarinetista. _____

4. Tú _____ guitarrista. _____

5. Antonia _____ doctora. _____

6. El Sr. y la Sra. de Morales _____ fotógrafos. _____

B2. En la aduana (*At customs*)

The customs officer has asked two tourists to show him various things they are carrying in their bags. Write down what each tourist says, describing the contents of the luggage.

(a)
—¿Qué hay en el bolso?

—*Hay un lápiz, dos...*

_____

_____

(b)
—¿Qué hay en la maleta?

—Hay _____

_____

_____

C1. La casa de Roberto

Describe the numbered objects you see in Roberto's house. Use adjectives such as the following: **caro / barato / bonito / grande / nuevo / viejo.**

En el cuarto *(bedroom)* . . .

⮥ *hay muchos libros. Los libros son viejos.*

1. *También hay...*

2. *También hay...*

En la sala *(living room)* . . .

3. _____

4. _____

5. _____

En el garaje . . .

6. _____

7. _____

8. _____

Tus posesiones *(Your belongings)*

Briefly describe (1) two things you own (be specific), (2) two things you do not have, and (3) two things you would like to own (be specific here too).

(1) ⮥ *Tengo una bicicleta. Es vieja pero es muy buena.*

(2) ⮥ *No tengo grabadora.*

(3) ⮥ *Espero tener un coche muy grande.*

Nombre _____   Fecha _____

LECCIÓN 4   Un club internacional

B1. Excusas

Carlos invited his friends to help him paint his room . . . but no one is coming. Express this, providing a different excuse for each person.

⋈ Marina _*no viene. Tiene que visitar el museo con una amiga. (Tiene que hablar con el profesor... etc.)*_

1. Rafael _____

_____

2. tú _____

3. Maribel y Carmen _____

4. yo _____

5. nosotros _____

_____

V1. Los juegos olímpicos *(The Olympic Games)*

Imagine that you are a journalist covering the Olympic Games. Give the nationality and age of each of the following athletes, according to the model. Note: **un atleta** and **una atleta** = *athlete*.

Cuba (20)   México (19)   España (18)   USA (16)   Puerto Rico (17)   Cuba (22)   España (20)

⋈   1.   2.   3.   4.   5.   6.

⋈ Pedro Iriarte _*es un atleta cubano. Tiene veinte años*_ .

1. Claudio Estrada _____ .

2. José Luis Mendoza _____ .

3. Jane Ruby _____ .

4. Tania Barrera _____ .

5. Sergio Muñoz _____ .

6. Marisa Cruz _____ .

C1. En el club

Imagine that you are visiting a youth club in Puerto Rico. You want to know the names of the following people. Write out the questions you would ask, according to the model.

➣ ¿Quién es *la chica que canta? (¿Quién es la muchacha que tiene una guitarra?... etc.)*

1. ¿Quiénes son _____

2. _____

3. _____

4. _____

¡Un poco de lógica, por favor!

Write six sets of logical sentences, saying first what people want to do and then what they need in order to do it. Use elements of A, B and C, according to the model.

A	B	C
yo	hablar español bien	tener un coche
tú	visitar México	estudiar
Carlos	tener un coche italiano	tener un tocadiscos
Ana y Beatriz	ganar dinero	hablar español
nosotros	viajar	tener dinero
	mirar la televisión	tener un televisor
	escuchar discos	trabajar

➣ *Tengo ganas de viajar. Por eso, tengo que tener un coche.*

1. _____

2. _____

3. _____

4. _____

5. _____

6. _____

El rincón cultural

El zodíaco

Under which zodiac sign were you born? Do you believe in astrology? Many people think that our future and also our personalities are linked to our zodiac signs.

Read the names of the zodiac signs in Spanish and note which qualities (**las cualidades**) and which weaknesses (**los defectos**) people born under those signs are supposed to have. Write down any adjectives you do not understand and look them up in a dictionary.

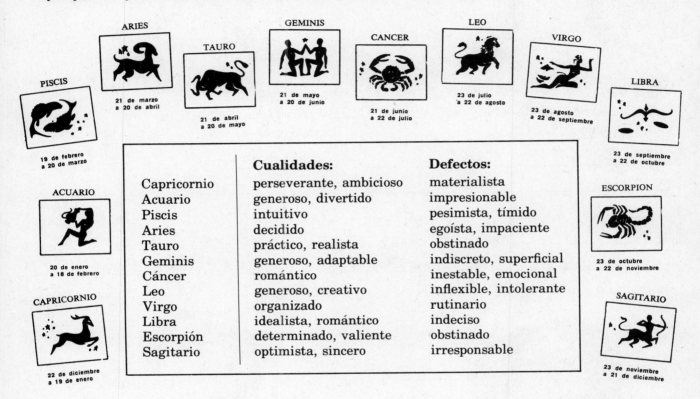

PISCIS
19 de febrero a 20 de marzo

ARIES
21 de marzo a 20 de abril

TAURO
21 de abril a 20 de mayo

GEMINIS
21 de mayo a 20 de junio

CANCER
21 de junio a 22 de julio

LEO
23 de julio a 22 de agosto

VIRGO
23 de agosto a 22 de septiembre

LIBRA
23 de septiembre a 22 de octubre

ACUARIO
20 de enero a 18 de febrero

CAPRICORNIO
22 de diciembre a 19 de enero

ESCORPION
23 de octubre a 22 de noviembre

SAGITARIO
23 de noviembre a 21 de diciembre

	Cualidades:	**Defectos:**
Capricornio	perseverante, ambicioso	materialista
Acuario	generoso, divertido	impresionable
Piscis	intuitivo	pesimista, tímido
Aries	decidido	egoísta, impaciente
Tauro	práctico, realista	obstinado
Geminis	generoso, adaptable	indiscreto, superficial
Cáncer	romántico	inestable, emocional
Leo	generoso, creativo	inflexible, intolerante
Virgo	organizado	rutinario
Libra	idealista, romántico	indeciso
Escorpión	determinado, valiente	obstinado
Sagitario	optimista, sincero	irresponsable

Now give the signs of the following people and say whether or not they have the qualities and weaknesses which the chart says are associated with their signs. Note: In the chart the adjectives are given in the masculine form. Be sure to use the feminine form when necessary.

Yo   Soy del signo ——————————————————————

Soy ————————————————————————————

No soy ——————————————————————————

Mi mejor amigo   Es del signo ——————————————————————

Es ——————————————————————————————

No es ——————————————————————————————

Mi mejor amiga   Es del signo ——————————————————————

Es ——————————————————————————————

No es ——————————————————————————————

¿Cómo son?

Look at each picture carefully. Then write a short paragraph describing each person. First say what the person looks like and give his or her approximate age. Describe the person's personality using the adjectives from the zodiac chart. Use your sense of psychology!!

Vilma Velasco
Calle 3. Oeste No. 53-87
Cali, Colombia

_____

_____

_____

_____

Roberto Oñoro
Avenida Lima 254 Chorrillos
Lima, Perú

_____

_____

_____

_____

Luisa Elvira Galván
Avenida 19 de abril, no. 7-113
San Cristóbal, Estado Táchua
Venezuela

_____

_____

_____

_____

Fernando García
Avenida General Primo de Rivera 108
Barcelona, España

_____

_____

_____

_____

Enrich your vocabulary through Spanish   the Latin connection

Many of the nouns, adjectives and verbs you have learned in this unit come from Latin.
There are many words in English which are derived from the same Latin roots. Match the
English words in parentheses with their corresponding definitions.

1. **amigo** (from the Latin **amicus:** *friend*)

   a.   a person who is friendly towards everyone: an _____ or

   _____ person

   b.   one who is unfriendly: an _____ person

   c.   friendship: _____
       (amiable   amicable   amity   unamiable)

2. **hombre** (from the Latin **homo:** *man, person*)

   a.   a person: a _____ being

   b.   mankind: _____

   c.   one who is kind toward other men and women: a _____ person

   d.   one who is concerned with the welfare of other persons: a _____

   e.   to deprive men and women of their qualities as persons: to _____
       (dehumanize   human   humane   humanitarian   humanity)

3. **joven** (from the Latin **juvenis:** *young*)

   a.   a young person: a _____

   b.   younger in age or rank: _____

   c.   to bring back one's youthful vigor and energy: to _____
       (junior   juvenile   rejuvenate)

4. **maestro** (from the Latin **magister:** *a person who is in charge, who gives orders, who controls or
   dominates*)

   a.   the person who is in charge of a school: the _____

   b.   the person who gives orders to a dog: the dog's _____

   c.   to dominate a problem: to achieve _____

   d.   an official who is in charge of the enforcement of the law:

   a _____
       (headmaster   magistrate   master   mastery)

5. **libro** (from the Latin **liber:** *book*)

   a.   a place where books are kept: a _____

   b.   a person who catalogs books: a _____
       (librarian   library)

6. **alto** (from the Latin **altus:** *high*)

   a. a singer with a high voice, compared to a tenor or baritone:

   an _____

   b. height above sea level: _____

   c. an instrument for measuring a plane's height above the ground:

   an _____

   (altimeter   altitude   alto)

7. **bajo** (from the Latin **bassus:** *low*)

   a. a stringed instrument which produces low notes: a _____ violin

   b. the lowest part of the house: the _____

   c. to lower the value of money: to _____ it

   d. a breed of dog with a very low build: a _____

   e. lowly (that is, not precious) metals: _____ metals

   (base   basement   bass   basset   debase)

8. **malo** (from the Latin **malus:** *bad*)

   a. a person who is in bad health: one who suffers from a _____

   b. a fatal or dangerous tumor: a _____ tumor

   c. bad will, with an intent to injure: _____

   d. something which is working badly or not at all: something which is

   _____

   (malady   malfunctioning   malice   malignant)

9. **nuevo** (from the Latin **novus:** *new*)

   a. a person who is new at something: a _____

   b. a new fad: a _____

   c. to make a house or room look like new: to _____ the place

   (novelty   novice   renovate)

10. **tener** (from the Latin **tenere:** *to have, to hold, to keep*)

    a. a teacher who holds a permanent position: one who has _____

    b. one who stubbornly holds on: a _____ person

    c. to get information: to _____ information

    d. to keep one's position: to _____ that position

    (maintain   obtain   tenacious   tenure)

TEST / REPASO   Unidad 3

ESTRUCTURA

Test 1   En la aduana *(At customs)*   The following passengers are going through customs, giving their nationality and the type of passport they are holding. Complete the sentences with the appropriate forms of **ser, venir** and **tener.** Fill in the last blank with the correct adjective of nationality: **francés / italiano / boliviano / colombiano / dominicano / chileno.**

⧖   Paco _____*es*_____ de Chile. _____*Viene*_____ de Santiago.
_____*Tiene*_____ un pasaporte _____*chileno*_____ .

1.   Nosotros _____ de Francia. _____ de París.
_____ pasaportes _____ .

2.   Tú _____ de Bolivia. _____ de La Paz.
_____ un pasaporte _____ .

3.   Yo _____ de Colombia. _____ de Bogotá.
_____ un pasaporte _____ .

4.   Uds. _____ de la República Dominicana. _____ de Santo
Domingo. _____ pasaportes _____ .

5.   Felipe y María _____ de Italia. _____ de Roma.
_____ pasaportes _____ .

Test 2   La orquesta de la escuela   Say who's who in the school orchestra by completing the sentences with the appropriate definite article. Be sure to distinguish between males and females.

⧖   ____*La*____ clarinetista es Ángela.

1.   _____ pianista es Ramón.

2.   _____ guitarristas son José y Roberto.

3.   _____ trompetera es Susana.

4.   _____ clarinetistas son Elena e Inés.

5.   _____ violinistas son Pablo, Isabel y Clara.

Test 3   Las similitudes *(Similarities)*   The people below have friends whose personality traits are similar to their own. Express this by completing the sentences with the appropriate forms of the indefinite article and the underlined adjectives.

⧖   Claudia es <u>simpática</u>. Tiene ____*un*____ novio ____*simpático*____ .

1.   Carlos es <u>dinámico</u>. Tiene _____ amigas _____ .

2.   Felipe y Luis son <u>generosos</u>. Tienen _____ amiga _____ .

3.   Teresa es <u>independiente</u>. Tiene _____ amigos _____ .

4.   Roberto y José son <u>sentimentales</u>. Tienen _____ amigas _____ .

5. Alberto y Tomás son <u>sinceros</u>. Tienen _____ amigo _____.

6. Luisa y María son <u>pacientes</u>. Tienen _____ amigo _____.

7. Enrique es <u>intelectual</u>. Tiene _____ novia _____.

8. Pablo es <u>popular</u>. Tiene _____ amigas _____.

9. Rafael es <u>pesimista</u>. Tiene _____ amigos _____.

10. Isabel es <u>generosa</u>. Tiene _____ amigos _____.

Test 4   El congreso estudiantil internacional   The students below are representing their countries at an international student congress. Give each student's nationality by completing the following sentences with the appropriate form of the indefinite article, the noun **estudiante,** and the appropriate adjective of nationality.

⊗ (Estados Unidos) Silvia es _una estudiante norteamericana_ .

1. (España)   Marisa es _____

2. (Cuba)   Alberto es _____

3. (México)   Eduardo y Federico son _____

4. (Puerto Rico) Maribel y Teresa son _____

5. (España)   Rafael y Manuel son _____

6. (España)   Beatriz e Isabel son _____

VOCABULARIO

Test 5   Los nuevos alumnos   There are two new students in your class. Describe them to a friend of yours, giving the characteristics mentioned below. Use complete sentences.

A. Silvia (16 años)   B. Carlos (15 años)

1. (age)   _____

2. (color of hair) _____

3. (height)   _____

4. (slimness)   _____

Nombre _____ Fecha _____

Test 6 Los objetos perdidos *(Lost and found)*   You are working in a lost-and-found office in the Bogotá airport. Name the various objects which have been brought in today.

✍ Hay *un radio* 1. _____, 2. _____, 3. _____,

4. _____, 5. _____, 6. _____, 7. _____,

8. _____, 9. _____ y 10. _____.

Test 7 Los opuestos se atraen *(Opposites attract one another)*   Match the adjectives on the left (numbers) with their opposites on the right (letters). Write the corresponding letter next to each adjective.

✍ simpático *B*

1. caro _____   A. viejo
2. grande _____   B. antipático
3. nuevo _____   C. rubio
4. bueno _____   D. inteligente
5. moreno _____   E. barato
6. divertido _____ F. bonito
7. delgado _____   G. gordo
8. feo _____   H. pequeño
9. tonto _____   I. aburrido
                       J. malo

COPYRIGHT © 1980 BY D.C. HEATH AND COMPANY   Unidad tres **51**

Test 8 Intérprete   You are acting as interpreter for an American journalist on assignment in a Mexican school. Indicate how the journalist should say the following sentences.

1. *How old are you?* _____

2. *Do you have to study much?* _____

3. *Do you have to work?* _____

4. *Do you feel like traveling?* _____

5. *How many books do you have?* _____

6. *How many tapes do you have?* _____

7. *There is a Mexican teacher.* _____

8. *There are thirty students.* _____

CULTURA

Test 9 ¿Sí o no?   Indicate whether the information in these statements is correct or not by circling **sí** or **no.**

sí   no   1. Anyone whom a Hispanic teenager meets at a party is immediately considered "un amigo" or "una amiga."

sí   no   2. Inviting a girl to the movies or to a restaurant can be more difficult for a Hispanic boy than for an American boy.

sí   no   3. In Spanish-speaking countries teenagers usually go out in groups, rather than in couples.

sí   no   4. Walking down the street with one's friends is a common leisure-time activity in Hispanic countries.

sí   no   5. In Spain and Latin America it is forbidden to sing in the streets.

sí   no   6. For Spanish speakers, "un americano" can be someone from Argentina as well as someone from the United States.

sí   no   7. The term "norteamericano" refers to people who live in Mexico.

sí   no   8. Madrid, the capital of Spain, is the largest Spanish-speaking city in the world.

UNIDAD 4

LECCIÓN 1   Un día de clases

A1. **¡No podemos hacerlo todo!** *(We can't do everything!)*

It is usually impossible to do two different things at the same time. Express this by completing the following sentences according to the model. Be sure to use the personal **a** when appropriate.

⟷   (las chicas / la profesora) Pedro mira _*a las chicas. No mira a la*_
   *profesora.*

1. (Antonio / el libro) Carmen mira _____

2. (Isabel / Lucía) Raúl espera _____

3. (el disco / Bárbara) Felipe escucha _____

4. (revistas / discos) Felicia compra _____

5. (el autobús / los chicos) Enrique espera _____

V1. **El intruso** *(The Intruder)*

The blank in each of the sentences below could logically be filled by two of the verbs listed under A, B and C. The third one would not make sense: it is the intruder. Look for the intruder and circle it.

		A	B	C
⟷	Carlos _____ un hotel.	mira	(escucha)	busca
1.	Los alumnos _____ el autobús.	esperan	compran	toman
2.	Nosotros _____ a María.	compramos	miramos	buscamos
3.	El autobús _____ a las dos.	enseña	viene	llega
4.	¿Qué _____ en el bolso?	llegas	tienes	llevas
5.	Isabel _____ el café.	compra	toma	habla
6.	Pedro _____ los monumentos.	busca	lleva	mira
7.	La Sra. de Ochoa _____ español.	habla	enseña	saca

B1. El día de los enamorados *(Saint Valentine's Day)*

Write out who is inviting whom and where they are going.

⟫ Paco (María / el teatro) *Paco invita a María al teatro.*

1. Roberto (la chica norteamericana / el club) _____

2. Los chicos (las chicas / el concierto) _____

3. Carmen (el chico mexicano / el café) _____

4. La profesora (el fotógrafo / el cine) _____

5. Las chicas (los chicos / la discoteca) _____

B2. Los chismosos *(Gossips)*

Say that the following people are talking about members of the opposite sex. Use the expression **hablar de** *(to talk about)*.

⟫ La chica *habla del chico* .

1. El chico _____ .
2. Las muchachas _____ .
3. La alumna _____ .
4. Los alumnos _____ .
5. La profesora _____ .
6. La mujer _____ .
7. Los estudiantes _____ .
8. La estudiante _____ .
9. El maestro _____ .
10. El hombre _____ .

LECCIÓN 2   Un fin de semana

A1.   ¿Dónde están?

People's occupations are sometimes a clue to where they are. Indicate who is at each of the following locations: **el museo** / **el teatro** / **el hospital** / **la farmacia** / **el laboratorio** / **la escuela** / **el aeropuerto** / **la universidad.** For each person, fill in the first blank with the appropriate form of **ser,** and then write a sentence using **estar.**

⊗   La Sra. de Montez ___*es*___ profesora.   *Está en la universidad .*

1.   Carlos y Enrique _____ actores. _____

2.   Tú _____ piloto. _____

3.   Yo _____ doctor. _____

4.   Ana y Marisa _____ turistas. _____

5.   Nosotros _____ alumnos. _____

6.   El Sr. García _____ farmacéutico *(pharmacist).* _____

7.   La Sra. de Durán _____ química *(chemist).* _____

C1.   ¡Un poco de lógica, por favor!

When someone goes somewhere, it is usually for a reason. Describe the objectives of the following people, using elements of columns A, B and C according to the model. Use **ir a** for the verb.

A	B	C
yo	la playa	estudiar
tú	el campo	hablar español
el estudiante	el café	hablar inglés
Clara y María	la tienda	mirar a los chicos
nosotros	el concierto	comprar una revista
	México	hablar con amigos
	los Estados Unidos	tomar una Coca-Cola
	la universidad	visitar Nueva York
		sacar fotos
		escuchar música clásica

⊗   *El estudiante va a la universidad. Va a estudiar.*

1.   _____

     _____

2.   _____

     _____

3.   _____

     _____

4.   _____

5. _____

_____

6. _____

_____

7. _____

_____

8. _____

_____

Una entrevista (An interview)

Imagine that a Spanish student is visiting your city. You are preparing an interview for the school paper. Prepare your questions in Spanish, being sure to use the appropriate verbs and question words. Address the student as tú.

1. *Are you Mexican?*   ¿_____?

2. *Where are you from?*   ¿_____?

3. *Where is your house?*   ¿_____ tu casa?

4. *Is it close to your school?*   ¿_____ tu escuela?

5. *Do you study much at home?*   ¿_____?

6. *Do you often go to your friend's house?*   ¿_____ a menudo _____ de

tu amigo?

7. *Where are you going during vacation?*   ¿_____ durante

las vacaciones?

8. *Are you going to New York?*   ¿_____?

9. *Are you going to visit Washington?*   ¿_____?

10. *Where are you going after that?*   ¿_____ después?

LECCIÓN 3 Correspondencia

A1. Los retratos *(Portraits)*

A good psychologist can often read faces and thereby discover a person's personality and feelings. Are you a good psychologist? Look at the following faces and say

a) how old you think the person is

b) what type of person he / she is: **simpático / antipático / serio / inteligente / interesante**

c) how the person now feels: **alegre / triste / contento / cansado**

d) . . . and (if you can) why the person feels that way.

1.   2.

María   *tiene 17 años.*

Es   *una chica seria.*

Ahora   *María está triste...*

porque   *no tiene dinero.*

1.   Juan Manuel _____.

Es _____.

Ahora _____.

porque _____.

2.   La Sra. de Camacho _____.

Es _____.

Ahora _____.

_____.

A2. El turismo en España

Various tourists are asking a policeman where certain places are and what they are like. The policeman looks in his notebook and answers them. Write out the dialogs.

T: *¿Dónde está el Hotel de Francia?*

P: *Está en la Plaza de la Independencia.*

T: *¿Es un hotel barato?*

P: *¡No, es un hotel muy caro!*

el Hotel de Francia	Plaza de la Independencia	
1. el Hotel Continental	calle de Colón	
2. el Café Inglés	calle de Segovia	
3. el Museo Azteca	Plaza Santo Domingo	
4. el restaurante Flamenco	calle Goya	

1. T: _____
   P: _____
   T: ¿_____ viejo?
   P: _____

2. T: _____
   P: _____
   T: ¿_____ grande?
   P: _____

3. T: _____
   P: _____
   T: ¿_____ pequeño?
   P: _____
   _____

4. T: _____
   P: _____
   T: ¿_____ caro?
   P: _____
   _____

B1. ¡Un poco de lógica!

If someone is in a movie theater, this person is probably watching a movie. Use this same type of logic and create five sentences using elements from columns A, B and C. Use the present participle of verbs in column C.

A	B		C	
yo	casa	la escuela	hablar con amigos	nadar
tú	el café	España	viajar	comprar discos
Pedro y Ricardo	la tienda	el campo	mirar a las chicas	bailar
nosotros	la piscina	la discoteca	sacar fotos	trabajar
			tomar café	estudiar

✍ *Tú estás en el café. Estás mirando a las chicas.*

1. _____
2. _____
3. _____
4. _____
5. _____

¿Quién soy yo?

Write a short letter to a Mexican pen pal describing yourself and some of your activities. Use the following questions as guidelines:

1. *What's your name?*   Me llamo _____.
2. *What is your nationality?*   _____
3. *How old are you?*   _____
4. *Are you tall? dark? ...*   _____
5. *Are you a good student?*   _____
6. *Where are you right now?*   _____
7. *Are you happy? tired? ...*   _____

LECCIÓN 4   ¿Eres un(a) buen(a) turista?

A1. ¡Qué decisión tan difícil! *(What a difficult decision!)*

Decide whether you will invite each of the following people to your class party or whether you will take him or her to the other event mentioned. What's your choice?

La invito a la fiesta. No la llevo _____ a la discoteca.
(No la invito a la fiesta. La llevo a la discoteca.)

1. _____ al cine.

2. _____ a la playa.

3. _____ al restaurante.

4. _____ a la cafetería.

5. _____ al concierto.

A2.   Unas cosas útiles

The people in column A are in class. Those in column B are going on vacation. Decide whether they each need the following objects. Use the verb **necesitar,** *to need.*

		A (en clase):	B (de vacaciones):
➤	los libros	Yo *los necesito* .	Carmen *no los necesita* .
1.	el radio	Los estudiantes _____ .	Alberto _____ .
		_____ .	_____ .
2.	los cuadernos	Nosotros _____ .	Tú _____ .
3.	la bicicleta	Andrés _____ .	Uds. _____ .
4.	el bolso	Tú _____ .	Yo _____ .
5.	la cámara	El profesor _____ .	Los turistas _____ .
6.	las revistas	Antonio _____ .	María _____ .
7.	el sol	Tú _____ .	Enrique _____ .
8.	el buen humor	Uds. _____ .	Ud. _____ .

A3. Las fotos de Ana

Miguel is looking at Ana's snapshots. He asks her to identify certain people. Write Ana's answers.

Elena y Luisa

Carmen

Inés y Esteban

Miguel: ¿Quién tiene el bolso?

Ana: *Lo tiene Carmen.*

1. M: ¿Quiénes escuchan los discos?

   A: _____

2. M: ¿Quiénes llevan las guitarras?

   A: _____

3. M: ¿Quiénes tienen el tocadiscos?

   A: _____

4. M: ¿Quién compra las revistas?

   A: _____

5. M: ¿Quiénes esperan el taxi?

   A: _____

B1. Mañana

When Susana asks Paco why he does not do certain things, Paco tells her he is going to do them tomorrow. Write out Paco's replies.

Susana: ¿No compras el periódico?

Paco: *Hoy no. Pero voy a comprarlo mañana.*

1. S: ¿No buscas las revistas?

   P: _____

2. S: ¿No invitas a los chicos?

   P: _____

3. S: ¿No escuchas la cinta?

   P: _____

4. S: ¿No estudias la lección?

   P: _____

El rincón cultural

¡Vamos a España!

Imagine that a Spanish pen pal has invited you to come to Spain. Since this is your first trip abroad, you want to know more about what you will be doing.

En el avión

First you will take a plane. You may want to choose IBERIA, which is the national airline of Spain. (The **Iberians** were early inhabitants of what is now Spain.) At the check-in counter, the employee will ask you to identify your suitcase with a tag like the one on the right. You may want to fill it in now!

La casa de cambio

Now that you have landed in Madrid and gone through customs, you are free to travel around Spain. But first you need to change your dollars into Spanish pesetas. The clerk at the bank will fill out a form similar to the one you see here.

Look at the form carefully. The person who used it changed $20 into pesetas.

1. What was the rate of exchange? (That is, how many pesetas does one receive for one dollar?)

   ———————————

2. How many pesetas did the person receive in exchange for twenty dollars? ———————————

3. At this rate of exchange, about how many pesetas would you receive if you were changing

   $10? ——————————— $100? ———————————

En el tren

If your Spanish pen pal lives outside of Madrid, the capital of Spain, you may have to take the train. In this case you would take the RENFE, which is the Spanish national railroad system. (RENFE stands for **Red Nacional de Ferrocarriles Españoles** or *National Network of Spanish Railroads*.)

At the station you would buy a ticket (**un billete**). Look at the RENFE ticket below. This ticket contains various types of information, such as:

número de tren	*train number*
fecha	*date*
clase	*class*
número de coche	*car number*
asiento	*seat*
hora de salida	*departure time*
tarifa	*rate*
precio (pts.)	*price (in pesetas)*

RENFE
EXPEDICION ELECTRONICA

BILLETE
AZ 261943

23 JUL 1976
Sello dependencia expendedora
SALAMANCA

NUM. DE TREN	FECHA	CLASE	NUM. DE COCHE	ASIENTO	HORA DE SALIDA	TARIFA	PRECIO PTS.

0164122907304017000023000011012911 68.
TER 29.07 1 G.1 S R C8.27 1C 667
3411C1041C1000304
NUM. DE CONTROL
DESDE-HASTA
SALAMANCA A MADRID CHM .EE

4. On the ticket, the departure date is shown as 29.07. What would the corresponding date be in English? _____

5. At what time does the train leave? _____

6. How many pesetas did the ticket cost? _____

   About how much is that in dollars? _____

7. Is this a first class or a second class ticket? _____

En el hotel

When you arrive at your destination, you may want to look for a hotel. Look at the hotel bill.

8. The hotel on this bill is named after a Spanish king. Which one? _____

9. The hotel is located in Salamanca. Can you find that city on a map of Spain?

10. If you wanted to reserve a room by telegram, which telegraph address would you use? _____

11. What is the phone number of the hotel? _____

12. How much does a room (**una habitación**) cost? _____ How much would this be in dollars? _____ Is it expensive? _____

13. How much does breakfast (**el desayuno**) cost? _____ How much would this be in dollars? _____ Is it expensive? _____

HOTEL - RESIDENCIA
ALFONSO X **HR** ***
SALAMANCA (España)
Las facturas se liquidarán semanalmente y los señores viajeros que no tengan equipaje lo harán diariamente

Dirección Telegráfica: ALFONSOTEL
Generalísimo Franco, 44
Teléfono 21 44 00
Habitación núm. 520
Nº 16859

Sr. D. VERONI HANLEY

A - SERVICIOS ORDINARIOS

Mes de X de 19 79	Día 28 Pesetas	Día 29 Pesetas	Día Pesetas	Día Pesetas	Día Pesetas	Día Pesetas	Día Pesetas	TOTALES Pesetas
Habitación	780							
Desayuno.		168						
Cama supletoria								
Total del día, pesetas	780	168						
Suma anterior		780	948					
Total servicios ordinarios .								948

Enrich your vocabulary through Spanish   the Latin connection

Many of the Spanish words you have learned in this unit come directly from Latin. English contains many words which have the same Latin roots. Match the English words in parentheses with their corresponding definitions.

1. **campo** (from the Latin **campus:** *field, meadow*)

    a. the fields or grounds of a school or college: the _____

    b. to pitch a tent in an open field: to _____

    c. a field area where many persons have set up tents: an _____
        (camp   campus   encampment)

2. **mar** (from the Latin **mare:** *sea*)

    a. a basin for sea-going boats: a _____

    b. the Canadian provinces of Nova Scotia, New Brunswick and Prince Edward Island, which

        are near the sea: the _____ Provinces

    c. a ship that navigates under the sea: a _____

    d. a sailor or seaman: a _____

    e. pertaining to the sea: _____
        (marina   marine   mariner   Maritime   submarine)

3. **piscina** (from the Latin **piscina:** *fish pond)*

    a. the twelfth sign of the Zodiac, portrayed by two fish: _____

    b. pertaining to fishing: _____
        (Pisces   piscatorial)

4. **pueblo** (from the Latin **populus:** *people*)

    a. the total number of people living in a given place: the _____

    b. one who is liked by many people: a _____ person

    c. to remove the people from an area: to _____

    d. an adobe village in the Southwest: a _____
        (depopulate   popular   population   pueblo)

5. **barco** (from the Latin **barca:** *boat*)

    a. a large flat boat: a _____

    b. to get onto a ship and leave on a trip: to _____

    c. to get off a ship: to _____

    d. a wharf in San Francisco where ships are docked: the _____
        (barge   disembark   Embarcadero   embark)

6. **enfermo** (from the Latin **infirmus**: *weak*)

    a.   a place which cares for weak, sick people: _____

    b.   physical weaknesses: _____

    c.   a decision which is not weak is: a _____ decision

                (firm   infirmary   infirmities)

7. **avión** (from the Latin **avis**: *bird*)

    a.   an enclosure where birds are kept: an _____

    b.   a person who flies a plane (and may be likened to a bird):

         an _____

    c.   the operation of aircraft: _____

    d.   pertaining to birds: _____

              (avian   aviary   aviation   aviator)

TEST / REPASO   Unidad 4

ESTRUCTURA

Test 1   De viaje *(Traveling)*   The following people are traveling through Spain. Say where they are today and where they are going tomorrow. Fill in the blanks with the appropriate forms of **estar** and **ir.**

⟫ Ud. _____*está*_____ en Málaga. _____*Va*_____ a Gibraltar.

1. Carlos _____ en Madrid. _____ a Toledo.

2. Yo _____ en Sevilla. _____ a Cádiz.

3. El Sr. Sánchez _____ en Córdoba. _____ a Granada.

4. Los estudiantes _____ en Santander. _____ a Oviedo.

5. Tú _____ en Alicante. _____ a Murcia.

6. Felipe y yo _____ en Barcelona. _____ a Valencia.

Test 2   En el café   There are many things one can do in a café. Describe what the following people are doing by indicating whether the spaces below should be filled in with **a** or whether they should be left blank   (—).

⟫ Pedro espera _____—_____ el autobús.

⟫ Nosotros buscamos _____*a*_____ Pedro.

1. Carlos mira _____ Carmen.

2. Carmen espera _____ José.

3. Lucía escucha _____ un disco.

4. Felipe escucha _____ los chicos.

5. Silvia mira _____ una revista.

Test 3 Un concurso de fotografía *(A photo contest)*   The following people are planning to enter a photography contest. Say that they are going to the places indicated below in order to photograph them. Fill in the first blank with the appropriate form of **a** + definite article, and the second blank with the appropriate form of **de** + definite article.

1.   (la avenida San Martín)   Carlos va _____ avenida San Martín.

        Saca una foto _____ avenida San Martín.

2.   (el museo azteca)   Susana va _____ museo azteca.

        Saca una foto _____ museo azteca.

3.   (las ruinas indias)   Pedro va _____ ruinas indias.

        Saca una foto _____ ruinas indias.

Test 4 Descripciones   Complete the descriptions by filling in the blanks with **es** or **está**, as appropriate.

1.   Federico _____ español. _____ de Madrid. Ahora _____ en los Estados Unidos.

2.   Carmen _____ una alumna muy seria, pero hoy no _____ en la escuela porque _____ enferma. ¡Qué malo!

3.   Rafael _____ un chico muy simpático. Ahora _____ en la playa con Pilar. _____ muy contento.

4.   La chica que _____ en el café se llama Yolanda. Yolanda _____ triste porque Pedro no _____ con ella.

5.   ¿_____ estudiando Carlos? ¡Él, no! No _____ en casa. _____ nadando con unos amigos.

6.   El coche que _____ en la calle _____ un coche italiano. _____ bonito pero _____ muy caro.

Test 5 Las vacaciones   It is vacation time. Describe what the following people are doing, using the present progressive form of the suggested verbs.

ᘒ Paco (nadar)   *Paco está nadando.*

1.   Elena (nadar)   _____

2.   nosotros (nadar)   _____

3.   Felipe (hablar con Susana)   _____

4.   Raquel y Elena (sacar fotos)   _____

5.   el Sr. Velázquez (viajar)   _____

6.   tú (mirar la televisión)   _____

Test 6   De compras (*Shopping*)   Luisa is going shopping. She is buying only the things which are cheap (**barato**) rather than expensive (**caro**). Express this by completing the sentences with the appropriate object pronouns and the negative **no** when appropriate.

⊗   La cámara es cara.   Luisa *no la*_____ compra.

1.   Los discos son baratos.   Luisa _____ compra.

2.   Las cintas son caras.   Luisa _____ compra.

3.   El reloj es caro.   Luisa _____ compra.

4.   La revista es barata.   Luisa _____ compra.

5.   El lápiz es barato.   Luisa _____ compra.

VOCABULARIO

Test 7   El intruso (*The intruder*)   The following sentences can be completed logically by two of the words in each set of parentheses. One word does <u>not</u> fit; this is the **intruso**. Circle it.

⊗   Voy a la escuela en ____.   (bicicleta / autobús / (radio))

1.   Voy a la ____ porque me gusta nadar.   (playa / piscina / plaza)

2.   En la ____ Santo Tomás hay un restaurante bueno. (iglesia / calle / plaza)

3.   Pablo está ____ porque tiene muchos amigos simpáticos. (triste / alegre / contento)

4.   No voy a la fiesta porque estoy ____. (contento / cansado / enfermo)

5.   María ____ un lápiz. (busca / compra / nada)

6.   ____ a Anita. (Espero / Busco / Tomo)

7.   ¿Vas a ____ el tocadiscos? (llevar / comprar / llegar)

8.   Voy a ir a Puerto Rico en ____. (avión / tren / barco)

Test 8   Intérprete   Translate the following sentences for a Spanish friend who knows no English.

1.   *Where do we go now?* _____

2.   *Where do you work?* _____

3.   *Where are you from?* _____

4.   *Are you going to the beach?* _____

5.   *Are you at the beach?* _____

6.   *I am going home.* _____

7.   *I am going to Pedro's house.* _____

8.   *I am going to swim. And you?* _____

9.   *Are you going to swim with us?* _____

10.   *Pedro is going to take pictures.* _____

11.   *When are you going to visit Madrid?* _____

CULTURA

Test 9 **¿Sí o no?**   Indicate whether the information contained in the statements below is true or false by circling **sí** or **no.**

sí   no   1. A "colegio" is a small university.

sí   no   2. In Spanish-speaking countries, most of the private schools are Catholic.

sí   no   3. There are separate private schools for boys and girls.

sí   no   4. Hispanic teenagers enjoy music and dancing.

sí   no   5. It was the Spaniards who introduced the first musical instruments to the New World.

sí   no   6. Quetzalcoatl, the plumed serpent, was worshiped as a god by the Indians of Mexico.

sí   no   7. Today most Mexican-Americans live in California, Texas and the Southwest.

sí   no   8. Because of the very hot climate, few Americans visit Mexico.

sí   no   9. When the Spaniards came to Mexico, they taught the Indians how to build stone pyramids.

sí   no   10. Mexico was conquered by the Spaniards about 150 years after Columbus came to America.

UNIDAD 5

LECCIÓN 1   Olivia Ortiz, puertorriqueña de Nueva York

A1.   A distancia . . .

The following people are commuters. Say that they do not live where they work. Fill in the first blank with the appropriate form of **trabajar** and the second blank with the appropriate form of **vivir**.

1. El Sr. Morales _____ en Los Ángeles, pero _____ en Santa Ana.

2. Yo _____ en el centro, pero _____ en el campo.

3. Muchos españoles _____ en Francia, pero _____ en España.

4. Muchos mexicanos _____ en los Estados Unidos, pero _____ en México.

(Now write a sentence about a commuter you know.)

5. _____ en _____, pero _____ en _____.

A2.   En la biblioteca *(In the library)*

The people on the left are reading. Those on the right are writing. Fill in the blanks with the appropriate forms of **leer** and **escribir**.

1. Yo _____ un periódico.

2. Nosotros _____ una novela.

3. Carmen _____ el *ABC*.

4. Tú _____ *Hoy*.

5. Juan y Ana _____ poemas.

Isabel _____ una carta.

Uds. _____ tarjetas.

Yo _____ un poema.

Ud. _____ una carta.

Luis y Pedro _____ composiciones.

B1.   ¡Es lógico!

Of the three verbs in parentheses, only two logically complete the sentences. Choose the correct verb for each blank and write in the appropriate form.

➢ (creer, comer, leer) ¿Por qué ____*lee*____ María el periódico? ¿____*Cree*____ ella en el horóscopo?

1. (vivir, aprender, creer) Yo _____ en España, donde _____ español.

2. (beber, comer, vender) Miguel está en un restaurante mexicano. _____ café y _____ unas tortillas.

3. (vender, beber, trabajar) El mecánico _____ en una estación de servicio. _____ gasolina.

4. (comprender, ver, hablar) ¿_____ los alumnos cuando el profesor _____ español?

5. (leer, ver, creer) ¿_____ Ud. a la chica? Yo _____ que es María.

6. (comprender, leer, vivir) Nosotros _____ un poema pero no lo _____. ¡Qué lástima!

7. (aprender, comprender, asistir) ¡Yo no _____ por qué tú _____ francés!

8. (escribir, vivir, asistir) Carlos y Ramón _____ en Nueva York. _____ a una escuela bilingüe.

C1. ¿Sabes observar? *(Do you know how to observe?)*

Study the following pictures and then say to whom the numbered objects belong.

el Sr. López   María   Rafael

Es el bolso del Sr. López. _____

1. _____

2. _____

3. _____

4. _____

5. _____

6. _____

LECCIÓN 2 Las fotos de Amalia

A1. El árbol genealógico *(The family tree)*

Complete your family tree by writing the names and relationships of your relatives in the boxes below. (You may use a separate sheet of paper and add extra boxes as needed.)

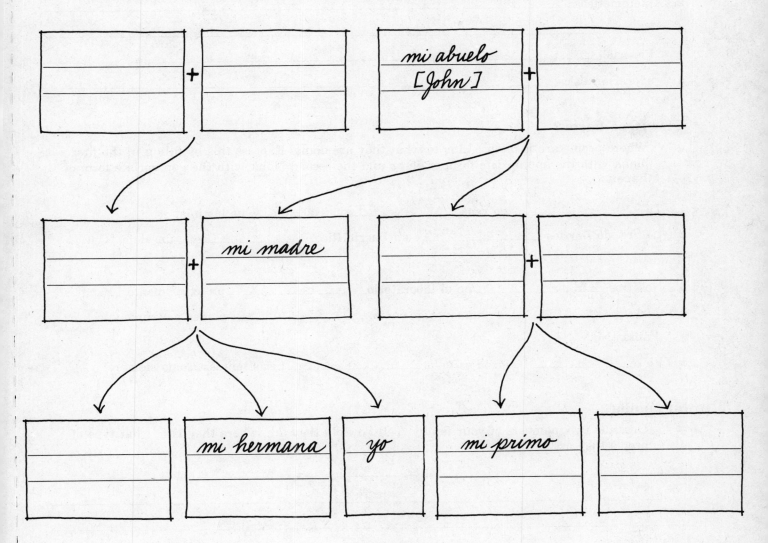

A2. Paco y Ana

Paco borrows a lot of things but does not return them. When he asks Ana where her things are, she tells him that other people have them. Complete the dialog according to the model.

Paco:

Ana:

⊗ ¿Dónde están ___*tus*___ discos?   ¿_*Mis discos*_? ___*Los tiene*___ Rafael.

1. ¿Dónde está _____ grabadora?   ¿_____? _____ María.

2. ¿Dónde están _____ cintas?   ¿_____? _____ Pedro.

3. ¿Dónde está _____ reloj?   ¿_____? _____ Isabel.

4. ¿Dónde están _____ libros?   ¿_____? _____ Marisol.

B1. Los profesores

Before going to Parents' Night, your parents ask you the names of your teachers. Answer them according to the model.

✍ español: *Mi profesor(a) de español es el Sr. (la Srta.) Sánchez.*

1. inglés: _____

2. matemáticas: _____

3. ciencias: _____

4. historia: _____

5. educación física: _____

C1. ¿Qué hacen?

Where people are is often a clue to what they are doing. Express this by filling in the first blank with the appropriate form of **estar** and the second blank with the appropriate form of **hacer.**

1. Tú _____ en casa. _____ la tarea. ¡Qué lástima!

2. La Sra. de Barrios _____ en Puerto Rico. _____ un viaje. ¡Qué suerte tiene!

3. Nosotros _____ en el laboratorio. _____ un experimento. ¡Bang!

4. Carlos _____ con su (his) novia. ¡_____ planes matrimoniales! ¡Fantástico!

5. Yo _____ en la escuela. _____ cosas tontas. ¡Como siempre!

Mi familia

Describe two members of your family. Tell how old they are, where they live, what type of people they are, etc.

_____

_____

_____

_____

_____

_____

_____

LECCIÓN 3   El edificio de apartamentos

V1.   El maratón

You are reporting on a marathon for a local Spanish-language radio station. Announce the arrivals of the following runners, according to the model.

⮕ *El primero es el número siete.* _____

1. _____
2. _____
3. _____
4. _____
5. _____
6. _____
7. _____
8. _____
9. _____

A1.   ¿Haces lo que dices? *(Do you do what you say?)*

The people below do things similar to what they say. Express this according to the model.

⮕ Mis hermanos ___*dicen*___ cosas tontas.   *También hacen cosas tontas.*

1. Mi mamá _____ cosas interesantes. _____
2. Yo _____ cosas inteligentes. _____
3. Mis amigos _____ cosas cómicas. _____
4. La profesora _____ cosas divertidas. _____
5. Nosotros _____ cosas extraordinarias. _____
6. Tú _____ tonterías *(foolish things)*. _____

B1. En el depósito de equipaje *(In the baggage room)*

The train has arrived and the following people are going to the baggage room to pick up their things. Express this according to the illustrations.

1. María *va a buscar su radio, su...*

2. Carlos _____

3. La Sra. de Barrios _____

4. Manuel y Anita _____

B2. En el café

In the café Paco meets two people: his friend Eduardo and Anita, Eduardo's girl friend. Obviously Paco addresses Eduardo as **tú**, but since he does not know Anita well, he addresses her as **Ud.** During the conversation he asks Eduardo and Anita the same questions, but in a somewhat different manner. Write the questions.

(Eduardo = tú)

✗ Paco: ¿Cómo está ___*tu*___ papá?

1. ¿Cómo están _____ hermanos?

2. ¿Vas a invitar a _____ primo a la fiesta?

3. ¿Ves a _____ amigos franceses a menudo?

4. ¿Tienes _____ discos contigo?

(Anita = Ud.)

¿ *Cómo está su papá* ?

¿ _____ ?

¿ _____ ?

¿ _____ ?

¿ _____ ?

Tu casa

Describe the following aspects of your house. You may use adjectives such as the following: **moderno / viejo / nuevo / pequeño / grande / confortable**.

✗ *Nuestra* casa *es pequeña (confortable, etc.)*

1. _____ cocina _____

2. _____ comedor _____

3. _____ sala _____

4. _____ cuartos _____

5. _____ televisor _____

LECCIÓN 4 ¿Eres servicial?

A1. En el aeropuerto

Many people are at the airport. Some are with their families or friends and others are waiting for friends who are arriving. Complete the sentences below with the appropriate possessive adjectives.

✏ María espera a ___*su*___ mamá y a ___*sus*___ hermanos.

1. Roberto espera a _____ novia.

2. Antonia busca a _____ novio y a _____ padres.

3. Llegamos con _____ amigos y _____ hermanos.

4. Saco fotos de _____ prima, _____ hermanos, _____ padres y _____ perro.

5. El Sr. Ordóñez llega con _____ esposa y _____ hijos.

C1. Consejos (Advice)

People give all types of advice. Say whether the following people give excellent (**excelentes**), good (**buenos**) or bad (**malos**) advice.

✏ Mi mamá *da buenos consejos* _____.

1. Mi papá _____.

2. Mis amigos _____.

3. El profesor (La profesora) _____.

4. Yo _____.

5. Nosotros _____.

D1. La lotería (The lottery)

Imagine you have just won ten thousand pesetas in a Spanish lottery. With your money you have bought the following gifts. Say to whom you will give each present.

✏ A mi papá *le doy el coche (la cámara, etc.)* _____

1. A mis hermanos _____

2. A mi mamá _____

3. A mi mejor amigo _____

4. A mi mejor amiga _____

5. Al profesor (A la profesora) de español _____

6. A los alumnos de la clase _____

D2. El mundo de Manuel

Manuel has divided the world into two categories: the people he likes (A) and the people he does not like (B). Describe how he acts with the people in each group, according to the model.

A   B

➤ *La* invita al cine.   *No lo invita al cine.*

1. _____ escribe.   _____

2. _____ llama por teléfono.   _____

3. _____ ayuda.   _____

4. _____ da buenos consejos (advice).   _____

5. _____ dice cosas divertidas.   _____

6. _____ manda cartas.   _____

¿Te importa la gente? *(Do people matter to you?)*

Of course you care about other people. Write three things you would do for the following people in the circumstances described. You may consider using the following verbs:
ayudar / llamar / dar / mandar / prestar / escribir / hablar / visitar / invitar.

➤ Mi mejor amigo está triste. *Lo ayudo. Lo llamo por teléfono.*
Le hablo.

1. Mi tío está enfermo. _____

_____

2. Mis vecinos *(neighbors)* están en el hospital. _____

_____

3. Mis amigas están de mal humor. _____

_____

4. Mi mejor amiga necesita ayuda *(help)* para organizar una fiesta. _____

_____

El rincón cultural
Apellidos

Bernardo Peña Bernal

Bernardo Peña attends the University of Bogotá where he is studying law. Note how his complete name, Bernardo Peña Bernal, is given on his card. In many Hispanic countries, people often use the names of both parents.
- Peña is the family name of Bernardo's father.
- Bernal is the maiden name of his mother.

Un anuncio de nacimiento
This is the card which Bernardo's parents sent to their friends to announce the birth of their son.

ME LLAMO BERNARDO

NACI EL 13 DE SEPT. DE 1959

EN LA CLINICA LA MERCED

MIS PAPAS SON:

Alfredo Peña Ogliastri
Isabelita Bernal de Peña

1. Where was Bernardo born? _____
_____

2. How old is he? _____

3. What is the complete name of his father?
_____

4. What is the maiden name of his father's

mother? _____

Note the complete name of Bernardo's mother: Isabelita Bernal de Peña. In many Hispanic countries, a married woman keeps her maiden name (Bernal) and adds the word **de** plus the name of her husband (Peña).

Now imagine that you were born in Spain. Write your own birth announcement the way it would have appeared by completing the following card:

Me llamo _____

Nací el _____

Mis papás son: _____

_____

_____

Una esquela matrimonial

Imagine that Mari Carmen Almodóvar is a good friend of yours. Last year she was engaged to Juan Manuel Morales. Today you received the wedding announcement:

5. In what city is the wedding going to be performed? _____

6. In what church is the wedding going to take place? _____

7. On what day? _____

8. At what time? _____

9. Where is the reception going to be held?

_____

The wedding invitation provides information about the families of the bride and groom. Read it carefully and complete the following table.

los padres de Mari Carmen

el nombre de su papá: _____

el apellido (last name) de su papá: _____

el apellido de su abuela paternal: _____

el nombre de su mamá: _____

el apellido de su mamá: _____

los padres de Juan Manuel

el nombre de su papá: _____

el apellido de su papá: _____

el apellido de su abuela paternal: _____

el nombre de su mamá: _____

el apellido de su mamá: _____

Enrich your vocabulary through Spanish the Latin connection

Many of the Spanish words you have learned in this unit come directly from Latin. English contains many words which have the same Latin roots. Match the English words in parentheses with their corresponding definitions.

1. **beber** (from the Latin **bibere:** *to drink)*

   a. what a child wears so as not to dirty his/her clothes when drinking:

       a _____

   b. to drink: to _____

   c. a liquid refreshment or drink: a _____

       (beverage   bib   imbibe)

2. **comer** (from the Latin **comedere:** *to eat up)*

   a. something which is edible or can be eaten: a _____ item

   b. food: _____

       (comestible   comestibles)

3. **creer** (from the Latin **credere:** *to believe)*

   a. something that is hard to believe: something _____

   b. someone who believes everything: a _____ person

   c. someone whom people do not believe in: someone who has lost all

       _____

   d. What you carry to establish belief in your identity: _____

       (credibility   credulous   incredible   credentials)

4. **decir** (from the Latin **dicere:** *to say, tell)*

   a. to say what another person should write: to _____

   b. a person who tells the people of a country what to do: a _____

   c. the choice and use of words in speech: _____

   d. to say in advance what will happen: to _____

       (dictate   diction   dictator   predict)

5. **escribir** (from the Latin **scribere:** *to write)*

   a. the type of writing done by young children: _____

   b. a person who writes for someone else: a _____

   c. a written text: a _____

       (scribbling   scribe   script)

6. **leer** (from the Latin **legere:** *to read)*

    a.   a signature which one can read: a _____ signature

    b.   a prepared text meant to be read aloud: a _____

    c.   a letter which is impossible to read: an _____ letter

              (illegible   lecture   legible)

7. **vender** (from the Latin **vendere:** *to sell)*

    a.   a person who sells things: a _____

    b.   a machine which sells items: a _____ machine

              (vending   vendor)

8. **ver** (from the Latin **videre:** *to see)*

    a.   which cannot be seen: _____

    b.   the distance one can see under certain conditions: _____

    c.   a magnetic recording of what is seen and heard: a _____

              (invisible   videotape   visibility)

9. **madre** (from the Latin **mater:** *mother)*

    a.   a mother's love: _____ love

    b.   a hospital ward for mothers and babies: a _____ ward

              (maternal   maternity)

10. **padre** (from the Latin **pater:** *father)*

    a.   a father's discipline: _____ discipline

    b.   the practice of treating people in a fatherly manner: _____

              (paternal   paternalism)

11. **primero** (from the Latin **primarius:** *first, principal)*

    a.   the first coat of paint: the _____

    b.   the first set of elections: the _____

    c.   the first school one attends: _____ school

    d.   the first and most important member of the cabinet: the _____

    minister

              (prime   primer   primaries   primary)

12. **octavo** (from the Latin **octavus:** *eighth)*

    a.   a span of eight notes: an _____

    b.   a figure with eight sides: an _____

    c.   formerly the eighth month of the year (before the addition of July and August):

    _____

              (octagon   octave   October)

TEST / REPASO   Unidad 5

ESTRUCTURA

Test 1   En la biblioteca *(At the library)*   Some people in the library are reading while others are writing. Say what the following people are doing by filling in the blanks with the appropriate forms of **leer** and **escribir**.

leer:

1. Sara _____ un periódico.

2. Mis hermanos _____ una revista.

3. El profesor Ramos _____ un libro.

4. Tú _____ una novela.

5. Yo _____ un poema.

6. Nosotros _____ el diccionario.

escribir:

Yo _____ una carta.

La profesora Onís _____

una tarjeta.

Nosotros _____ un poema.

Mi hermana _____ con un

bolígrafo.

Consuelo _____ en su

cuaderno.

Tú _____ una novela.

Test 2   De venta *(For sale)*   The people below are selling some of their belongings. Express this by completing the sentences with the appropriate possessive adjectives.

➳ Tengo una guitarra. Vendo ____*mi*____ guitarra.

1.   Tengo unos discos. Vendo _____ discos.

2.   Paco tiene una bicicleta. Vende _____ bicicleta.

3.   El Sr. Montero tiene una casa. Vende _____ casa.

4.   Tenemos unos libros. Vendemos _____ libros.

5.   Tienes un diccionario. Vendes _____ diccionario.

6.   Carlos y yo tenemos una grabadora. Vendemos _____ grabadora.

7.   Mis primos tienen una moto. Venden _____ moto.

8.   Mi hermana tiene unas revistas. Vende _____ revistas.

9.   Uds. tienen una cámara. Venden _____ cámara.

10.   Sra. de Ochoa, ¿tiene Ud. unas cintas? ¿Vende Ud. _____ cintas?

Test 3   Actividades   Say what the following people are doing by completing the sentences with the appropriate forms of the verbs in parentheses.

A.   (hacer)   1.   Yo _____ la tarea.

2.   Mis padres _____ un viaje a México.

3.   Carmen _____ un viaje a Puerto Rico.

4.   Carlos y yo _____ la tarea de inglés.

5.   Y tú, ¿qué _____?

B.   (decir)   1.   Yo siempre _____ cosas interesantes.

2.   Mi hermano _____ cosas aburridas.

3.   Mis primas _____ la verdad.

4.   María y yo _____ que el profesor es inteligente.

5.   Y tú, ¿qué _____?

C.   (dar)   1.   Teresa _____ una fiesta.

2.   Yo le _____ un regalo.

3.   Mi hermana le _____ unos discos.

4.   Mis amigos le _____ unas cintas.

5.   Y tú, ¿qué le _____ a ella?

Test 4   La amiga ideal   Ana does a lot for her friends. Tell what she does for the people in parentheses by completing the sentences with the appropriate direct or indirect object pronoun.

_Lo_ (Felipe)   _Lo_ invita al cine.

1.   (Enrique)   _____ ayuda con la tarea.

2.   (Raquel)   _____ da sus revistas.

3.   (mi primo)   _____ llama por teléfono.

4.   (mi hermana)   _____ escribe para su cumpleaños.

5.   (Rafael)   _____ presta su tocadiscos.

6.   (Elena e Isabel)   _____ manda regalos.

7.   (mis amigos)   _____ invita a menudo a su casa.

8.   (Marisela)   _____ presta sus discos.

9.   (Clara)   _____ ayuda.

10.   (sus amigas)   _____ lleva al museo.

Test 5   Intérprete   Help a friend express the following sentences in Spanish.

1. *Where is Pedro's guitar?*   _____

2. *Where is Carmen's brother?*   _____

3. *Where are Sr. Ortega's friends?*   _____

4. *When is the Spanish class?*   _____

5. *Who is the music teacher?*   _____

6. *Do you have jazz records?*   _____

VOCABULARIO

Test 6   El intruso *(The intruder)*   Each of the following sentences can be logically completed by two of the verbs in the sets of parentheses. The one verb that does not fit is the intruder. Circle it.

∞ _____ con María.   (Estudio /(Invito)/ Hablo)

1. Felipe _____ francés.   (aprende / comprende / cree)

2. Carlos _____ a la playa.   (llega / vende / va)

3. Enrique _____ en Madrid.   (vive / está / asiste)

4. Marta _____ una carta.   (come / escribe / lee)

5. Raquel _____ Coca-Cola.   (cree / bebe / compra)

6. ¿Quién _____ los discos?   (come / vende / escucha)

7. No _____ a Carlos.   (creo / comprendo / bebo)

8. ¿ _____ al profesor?   (Ves / Vives / Miras)

9. No _____ dinero.   (ayudo / necesito / presto)

10. ¿Qué le _____ a Federico?   (das / prestas / buscas)

11. Raúl es un amigo bueno que _____ a sus   (ayuda / comprende / compra)

amigos.

12. Voy a _____ la tarjeta.   (mandar / escribir / ayudar)

Test 7   La familia   Write out the words which correspond to the following definitions.

∞ la esposa de mi tío = mi _*tía*_

1. el papá de mi madre = mi _____

2. la mamá de mi padre = mi _____

3. el hermano de mi papá = mi _____

4. las hijas de mi tío = mis _____

5. los hijos de mis padres = mis _____ y yo

Test 8   La arquitectura   Imagine that you are working for a Spanish architect. Complete the floor plan below by writing out the names of the numbered items. Be sure to use the proper definite article with each noun.

el jardín

1. _____
2. _____
3. _____
4. _____
5. _____
6. _____
7. _____
8. _____
9. _____

Test 9   El orden cronológico *(Chronological order)*   Complete the sentences below by writing out the appropriate ordinal number. As a guide, the numeral is indicated in parentheses.

Junio es el _____*sexto*_____ mes del año.   (6)

1. Adán es el _____ hombre.   (1)

2. Enero y febrero son los _____ meses del año.   (1)

3. John Adams es el _____ presidente de los Estados Unidos.   (2)

4. Marzo es el _____ mes del año.   (3)

5. Octubre es el _____ mes del año.   (10)

6. El sábado es el _____ día de la semana.   (7)

CULTURA

Test 10   ¿Sí o no?   Indicate whether the information contained in the statements below is true or false by circling **sí** or **no**.

sí   no   1.   San José is the capital of Puerto Rico.

sí   no   2.   There are more Puerto Ricans in New York than in San Juan.

sí   no   3.   Puerto Rico is often called "La Isla Encantada" (the enchanted island).

sí   no   4.   In Spanish, the term **familia** is limited to include only parents and children.

sí   no   5.   In Spanish-speaking countries, it is common for grandparents to live with their

children and grandchildren.

sí   no   6.   Caracas is the capital of Colombia.

sí   no   7.   It was in Caracas that the independence of Venezuela was proclaimed, in 1811.

sí   no   8.   For many Hispanic people Christmas (**la Navidad**) is the occasion for a big family

reunion.

UNIDAD 6

LECCIÓN 1   El problema del dinero

A1.   El chico vecino (The boy next door)

Imagine that your young neighbor asks you the following questions. Your answer will depend on whether you know him well and whether you like him or not. Write out your answers.

El vecino: Tú:

✏ ¿Me invitas a tu casa mañana?   *Sí, (No, no) te invito a mi casa.*

1.   ¿Me invitas al cine?   _____

2.   ¿Me enseñas tus fotos?   _____

3.   ¿Me ayudas con la tarea?   _____

4.   ¿Me hablas de tus planes?   _____

5.   ¿Vas a invitarme a tu fiesta

de cumpleaños?   _____

6.   ¿Vas a prestarme diez dólares?   _____

B1.   La gripe (The flu)

Carmen is in bed with the flu. The doctor has insisted that she neither do anything nor talk to anyone. Say what she's not doing by answering the questions below in the negative, using **nada** or **nadie** as appropriate.

1.   ¿Qué come Carmen? _____

2.   ¿Qué bebe Carmen? _____

3.   ¿A quién llama Carmen? _____

4.   ¿A quién invita a la casa Carmen? _____

5.   ¿Qué hace Carmen? _____

6.   ¿Con quién habla Carmen? _____

B2.   Nunca los domingos (Never on Sundays)

On Sundays the following people rest and never do any of the following things. Express this, using the negative word **nunca**.

✏ (trabajar)   Los domingos, yo *no trabajo nunca (...nunca trabajo)*

1.   (hacer las tareas)   Los domingos, María _____

2.   (ir a la escuela)   Los domingos, los chicos _____

3.   (comer en la cafetería)   Los domingos, tú _____

4.   (escuchar las cintas)   Los domingos, Paco y Raúl _____

5.   (hablar con el profesor)   Los domingos, nosotros _____

6.   (aprender cosas tontas)   Los domingos, yo _____

C1. ¿Cuánto dinero?

How much money do we ask from our parents? It depends on what we are buying. Say how much money the following people ask for in order to buy the items in parentheses.

⊗ (una bicicleta vieja)   Paco *pide treinta dólares* .

1. (una bicicleta nueva)   Carlos _____.

2. (un radio barato)   Felipe y Ana _____.

3. (una raqueta de ping pong)   Yo _____.

4. (una raqueta de tenis)   Tú _____.

5. (un cuaderno)   Manuela _____.

6. (un libro de español)   Ud. _____.

7. (un reloj barato)   Uds. _____.

8. (una calculadora)   Nosotros _____.

El presupuesto de la semana (The weekly budget)

Establish your own budget (or invent one) for a week. Record your income (ingresos) and your expenses (gastos) on a balance sheet. Then explain your budget.

⊗ Mi presupuesto: *Ingresos: Trabajo como niñera y gano 4.50 dólares. Mi mamá me da 3.00 dólares. Mi abuela me da 5.00 dólares. El total de mis ingresos es 12.50 dólares. Gastos: ...*

⊗ ingresos		gastos	
dinero de mi mamá	$3.00	cine	$2.00
regalo de mi abuela	5.00	disco	6.00
trabajo de niñera	4.50	revista	1.00
	12.50	helado	.50
		Coca-Cola	.30
			9.80

Mi presupuesto: _____

_____

ingresos	gastos

niñera (babysitter)

LECCIÓN 2 Los deportes

A1. En el estadio *(In the stadium)*

Say what types of sports the following people are playing, by filling in the blanks with the appropriate forms of **jugar**.

1. Nosotros _____ al volibol.

2. Tú _____ al tenis.

3. Francisco _____ al béisbol.

4. Las chicas _____ al básquetbol.

5. Yo _____ al tenis.

B1. Opiniones personales

Express your opinion about the items in Column A by using elements from columns B and C in logical affirmative or negative sentences. Feminine nouns are marked with an asterisk (*).

A		B	C
tenis	colección de sellos *(stamps)**	deporte	fantástico
música*	baile moderno	arte	interesante
escultura*	volibol	diversión*	aburrido
lectura*	natación*		
fútbol			

∅ *El tenis es un deporte interesante (... una diversión aburrida).*

1. La música _____.

2. _____

3. _____

4. _____

5. _____

6. _____

B2. Unas generalizaciones

Generalizations are often oversimplifications. However, we make them all the time. Generalize about the following aspects of life in the U.S., saying whether they are good or bad.

∅ restaurantes   *Los restaurantes norteamericanos son buenos (malos).*

1. música _____

2. política _____

3. café _____

4. coches _____

5. revistas _____

6. actrices _____

C1. Sí, pero . . .

We always find something to criticize, even in things we like. Say that you like the items below, but not the aspects in parentheses.

🖙 los estudios (la disciplina)

Me gustan los estudios . . . pero no me gusta la disciplina.

1. el cine (la violencia)

_____

2. la televisión (los programas aburridos)

_____

3. los deportes (los deportes violentos)

_____

4. las ciudades grandes (la contaminación del aire)

_____

C2. ¡Un poco de lógica, por favor!

There is always a reason for liking certain things. Express this by completing the sentences below, using the verb **gustar** and elements A and B. Look at the model carefully and be sure to use the appropriate pronouns: **me, te, le, les, nos.**

A		B	
ir al museo	mirar la televisión	los deportes	las enchiladas
ir al cine	comprar discos	las comedias musicales	el arte moderno
ir al estadio		la música	
ir a un restaurante mexicano		los programas de variedades (*variety shows*)	
tomar el avión			

🖙 Al Sr. López *le gusta ir al estadio porque le gustan los deportes.*

1. A mí _____.

2. A ti _____.

3. A Elena _____.

4. A nosotros _____.

Entre amigos

You want to know more about sports in Spain, so you ask a Spanish friend. Write your questions.

🖙 Are Spaniards active in sports?   *¿Son deportistas los españoles?*

1. *Do you like sports?* _____

2. *Does your school have a soccer team?* _____

3. *Are there good players in Spain?* _____

4. *Do you play tennis?* _____

5. *Do Spaniards play American football?* _____

LECCIÓN 3 Las diversiones y tú

B1. El valor del tiempo *(The value of time)*

Are you wasting your time when you watch TV? Your parents may think you are when your friends think you aren't. It's a matter of opinion. According to you, are the following people wasting their time? Respond, using the appropriate forms of **perder el tiempo.**

⇒ Carlos aprende francés. *(No) pierde el tiempo.*

1. Estudio español. _____

2. Isabel tiene una cita con un chico aburrido. _____

3. Paco lee el horóscopo. _____

4. Los chicos miran a las chicas. _____

5. Jugamos al tenis. _____

6. Duermes en la clase de matemáticas. _____

7. Uds. leen historietas *(comics).* _____

8. Vemos una película de «El gordo y el flaco» *(Laurel and Hardy).* _____

_____

C1. Citas

The following people have dates with their friends. They arrange to meet at the places indicated. Express this according to the model.

⇒ Silvia / Carlos / el parque *Silvia tiene una cita con Carlos.*
Lo encuentra en el parque.

1. Paco / Inés / su oficina _____

_____

2. Elena y Carmen / sus novios / el restaurante _____

_____

3. nosotros / unas amigas / las tiendas _____

_____

4. yo / Ramón / el cine _____

_____

5. tú / Isabel / el centro _____

_____

6. Uds. / unos amigos / la playa _____

_____

C2. ¡Yo!

Write about yourself. Use each of the verbs below in at least two affirmative or negative sentences. You may want to use the expressions suggested in parentheses.

☞ jugar (al fútbol / al tenis / al volibol / al ping pong / bien / mal)

Juego al tenis, pero no juego bien. Me gusta jugar al volibol. Juego bastante bien.

1. pensar (en el futuro / en mis estudios / en las vacaciones) _____

_____

2. perder (el tiempo / la paciencia / mis cosas) _____

_____

3. dormir (mucho / bien /mal / en la clase de . . .) _____

_____

4. entender (francés / español / inglés / a mis amigos / a los otros) _____

_____

5. contar (la verdad / el dinero / los cuentos) _____

_____

6. querer (ser famoso[a] / ayudar a otros / tener una familia grande / ser rico[a])_____

_____

Entre amigos

Imagine that your best friend asks you the following questions. Answer in Spanish.

☞ Do you want to play tennis? *¡Por supuesto quiero jugar al tenis!*

1. Do you want to go to the movies? _____

2. Do you prefer westerns or romantic movies? _____

3. How much does the movie cost? _____

4. When does the movie begin? _____

5. Do you understand me when I speak Spanish? _____

6. Do you remember who the actor is? _____

7. Can you lend me a dollar? _____

8. Can you lend me 100 dollars? _____

9. Can you meet me tomorrow? _____

10. Can you help me? _____

Nombre _____ Fecha _____

LECCIÓN 4   Los sábados por la noche

A1.   Los días de la semana

In English and Spanish, each day of the week has been named in honor of someone or something. Sunday is the day of the sun. Domingo is the "Day of the Lord" (from the Latin **Dominus** meaning *Lord*). Complete the sentences below with the appropriate days of the week, according to the model.

⟩⟩   *El miércoles es el día* _____ de Mercurio, el dios *(god)* del comercio . . . y de

los ladrones *(thieves)*.

1. _____ de Júpiter, el padre de los dioses.

2. _____ de la luna *(moon)*.

3. _____ de Venus, la diosa del amor *(love)*.

4. _____ de Marte, el dios de la guerra *(war)*.

A2.   La rutina

There are certain things we do or that happen on specific days of the week. Can you tell on which days the things mentioned below happen?

⟩⟩   Tengo la clase de español   *los lunes, los martes y los viernes* _____.

1.   Tengo la clase de matemáticas _____.

2.   Tengo la clase de inglés _____.

3.   Voy al cine con mis amigos _____.

4.   En casa, comemos espaguetis _____.

5.   Podemos ver los partidos de fútbol en la televisión _____.

6.   Hay ventas *(sales)* en el supermercado *(supermarket)* _____.

7.   No hay escuela _____.

B1.   La fiesta

Everyone is going out with someone to the party. Use your imagination and match the following people with those mentioned below, using **salir.**

Carmen / Luis / Cecilia y Laura / amigas mexicanas / Susana / Pedro

⟩⟩   Ramón   *sale con Susana* _____

1.   Felipe y José Antonio _____.

2.   Yo _____.

3.   Tú _____.

4.   Nosotros _____.

5.   Isabel _____.

B2. La maleta (*The suitcase*)

The objects that we can put into a suitcase should not be too big. Write whether the following people can fit their belongings into a regular-size suitcase. Use the appropriate forms of **poner**.

⊘ Alejandro tiene una guitarra. *No la pone en la maleta.*

1. Carmen tiene discos. _____

2. Tengo una cámara. _____

3. Tienes una bicicleta. _____

4. Mis primos tienen un televisor. _____

5. Nosotros tenemos un radio transistor. _____

6. Pedro tiene un piano. _____

C1. ¿Los reconoces? (*Do you recognize them?*)

Look at the portraits below. Most of us can recognize these people, but do not know them personally. Express this, using the appropriate forms of **conocer** and **reconocer** (*to recognize*), a verb conjugated like **conocer**.

⊘ (George Washington)   Paco   *lo reconoce... pero no lo conoce personalmente*

1. (John Travolta)   Mis amigos _____.

2. (Elizabeth Taylor)   Mi papá _____.

3. (Abraham Lincoln)   Tú _____.

4. (Los Beatles)   Yo _____.

5. (Jane Fonda)   Nosotros _____.

Entre amigos

You are exchanging correspondence with a Mexican pen pal. To improve her English, she writes to you in English. To improve your Spanish, you answer in Spanish. Answer her questions.

1. *Do you go out often?* _____

2. *With whom do you go out?* _____

3. *On which days of the week do you go out?* _____

4. *Do you have a car?* _____

5. *Do you drive a car? Whose car?* _____

6. *Do you have many records?* _____

7. *Do you take them to parties?* _____

8. *Do you know Hispanic boys?* _____

9. *Do you know Hispanic girls?* _____

El rincón cultural

¡Béisbol!

Baseball, the American national pastime, has become a very popular sport in many Hispanic countries, especially Cuba, Puerto Rico, the Dominican Republic, and Venezuela. It is also a favorite sport in many of the Hispanic communities in the United States.

Look at the ad on the right. This ad appeared in *El Diario* (the largest Spanish-language newspaper in the United States). In the ad the Goya food company salutes both fans and players on the opening of the 1978 season of the Federation of Amateur Hispanic Leagues.

Here is a small glossary of some of the words used in the ad:

la fanaticada	*the group of fans*
un pelotero	*a ball player*
una liga	*a league*
una temporada	*season*
un diamante	*(baseball) diamond*

GOYA Foods, Inc.
Saluda

A la gran Fanaticada hispana
y a los peloteros
de la Federación Amateur de Ligas Hispanas
quienes inauguran
la Temporada de Beisbol del 1978

este Domingo 16 de Abril, a las 12:00 del Mediodía
Diamante # 2, Parque Central, N.Y.C.
(Entrada calle 100 y C.P.W.)

y les recuerda
¡Si es GOYA... Tiene que Ser Bueno!

Many of the best players on the major U.S. teams are of Hispanic origin. The chart below gives the Spanish names of some of these teams. Read the names carefully and then fill in the names of the cities or states with which these teams are usually associated. Use a Spanish / English dictionary if you need one . . . and the sports pages of your newspaper!

LIGA AMERICANA

División este
a) los Tigres de *Detroit* _____

b) los Yankis de _____

c) los Indios de _____

d) los Azulejos de _____

División oeste
h) los Angelinos de _____

i) los Reales de _____

j) los Mellizos de _____

k) los Atléticos de _____

e) los Medias Rojas de _____

f) los Orioles de _____

g) los Cerveceros de _____

l) los Rancheros de _____

m) los Medias Blancas de _____

n) los Marineros de _____

División este

o) los Filis de _____

p) los Piratas de _____

q) los Cardenales de _____

r) los Expos de _____

s) los Mets de _____

t) los Cachorros de _____

División oeste

u) los Gigantes de _____

v) los Bravos de _____

w) los Padres de _____

x) los Dodgers de _____

y) los Astros de _____

z) los Rojos de _____

Para entender el béisbol en español

During the baseball season, most Hispanic newspapers and magazines published in the United States have a baseball section in which the games are described. In these accounts the following words often appear. Using the cues in parentheses, can you give the English equivalents of these words?

español:	inglés:	
un bateador	*batter*	(batear = to bat)
un lanzador	_____	(lanzar = to throw, pitch)
un hit	_____	
un sencillo	_____	(= una base)
un doble	_____	
un triple	_____	
un jonrón	_____	(= 4 bases)
un pasaporte	_____	(= cuando el bateador camina a la primera base)
una base robada	_____	(robar = to steal)
una carrera	_____	(correr = to run)
una entrada	_____	(= hay 9 entradas en un partido)

Now you can buy a Hispanic newspaper and read the baseball column!

Enrich your vocabulary through Spanish   the Latin connection

The following Spanish words from the unit are derived from Latin. There are many English words which have the same Latin roots. Match the English words in parentheses with their corresponding definitions.

1. **dormir** (from the Latin **dormire:** *to sleep)*

    a.   a building where students sleep: a _____

    b.   something which seems to be asleep: something _____

    (dormant   dormitory)

2. **conocer** (from the Latin **cognoscere:** *to know)*

    a.   a mission designed to know more about the enemy: a _____

    mission

    b.   a person who knows wine well: a wine _____

    c.   to know that a person you meet is familiar to you: to _____ that

    person

    d.   to travel so that people do not know who you are: to travel _____

    (connoisseur   incognito   recognize   reconnaissance)

3. **gastar** (from the Latin **vastare:** *to destroy*)

   a. to spend time on useless things: to _____ one's time

   b. to destroy an area: to _____ an area

   (devastate   waste)

4. **jugar** (from the Latin **jocare:** *to joke, to jest*)

   a. to play and throw several objects in the air at the same time:

   to _____

   b. to play a trick on someone: to play a _____

   c. funny, amusing: _____

   d. in a deck of cards, the one you can play for any other card:

   the _____

   (jocular   joke   joker   juggle)

5. **pedir** (from the Latin **petere:** *to ask, to seek*)

   a. a formal paper which requests action: a _____

   b. a person who makes a formal request: a _____

   (petition   petitioner)

6. **poner** (from the Latin **ponere:** *to put, to place*)

   a. to put money in the bank: to _____ money

   b. to put a dictator out of power: to _____ him

   c. to lay down your own rules: to _____ your rules

   d. the place where you put something: the _____ of that object

   (depose   deposit   impose   position)

7. **recordar** (from the Latin **recordare:** *to call to mind*)

   a. to tape or write down a conversation so that it can be remembered:

   to _____ the conversation

   b. information which helps people remember what happened in the past:

   historical _____

   (record   records)

8. **volver** (from the Latin **volvere:** *to turn around*)

   a. a pistol with a rotating chamber for bullets: a _____

   b. to move around the sun: to _____ around the sun

   c. a complete change in a political system: a _____

   d. the progressive change from simple to more complex forms of life:

   _____

   (evolution   revolution   revolve   revolver)

TEST / REPASO   Unidad 6

ESTRUCTURA

Test 1   Diálogos   Complete the following dialogs with the appropriate object pronouns.

A.   Elena: ¿Me invitas a tu fiesta?

    Carlos: Por supuesto. _____ invito siempre a mis fiestas.

B.   Felipe: ¿_____ dan mucho dinero tus padres?

    Marta: ¡No! _____ dan muy poco dinero.

C.   Enrique: Mañana es mi fiesta de cumpleaños. Voy a invitar a todos mis amigos.

    Susana y Luisa: Entonces _____ invitas, ¿verdad?

    Enrique: Claro, _____ invito, ¡pero no invito a sus novios!

D.   Sr. Ortiz: ¿_____ llama Ud. por teléfono mañana, Sr. Fonseca?

    Sr. Fonseca: ¡Claro! ¡_____ llamo a las diez!

Test 2   Expresión personal   Express your opinions about American people and things using the nouns and adjectives in parentheses.

➽   (literatura / ¿interesante?)   *La literatura norteamericana (no) es interesante.*

1.   (televisión / ¿interesante?)   _____

2.   (música / ¿muy buena?)   _____

3.   (fútbol / ¿violento?)   _____

4.   (chicos / ¿inteligentes?)   _____

5.   (chicas / ¿deportistas?)   _____

6.   (escuelas / ¿buenas?)   _____

Test 3   La crítica *(Criticism)*   Paco doesn't like anything. Complete the following dialog between Paco and his cousin Lucía by filling in the missing words.

1. Lucía: ¿Te gusta _____ volibol?

2. Paco: No, no _____ _____ deportes.

3. Lucía: ¿Te _____ los discos de los «Bee Gees»?

4. Paco: No, no _____ _____ música.

5. Lucía: ¿_____ _____ _____ películas del oeste?

6. Paco: ¡No, _____ _____ _____ cine!

Test 4 El sarampión *(Measles)*   Felipe has a bad case of measles. He cannot see or do anything. Express this by completing the sentences below with the necessary negative words.

1.   Felipe _____ hace _____.

2.   _____ invita a _____ a visitarlo.

3.   _____ come _____.

4.   _____ invita a Felipe al teatro.

5.   Felipe _____ mira _____ programa de televisión.

Test 5 El fin de semana   Describe what the following people are doing on the weekend. Complete the sentences below using the verbs in parentheses.

A.   (jugar)
1.   Yo _____ al tenis.

2.   Mis amigos _____ al volibol.

3.   Después, nosotros _____ al básquetbol.

4.   Y tú, ¿a qué _____?

B.   (pedir)
1.   Yo le _____ su moto a mi hermano.

2.   Francisco le _____ dinero a su papá.

3.   Mis amigos les _____ el coche a sus padres.

4.   Nosotros le _____ su guitarra a Carlos.

C.   (encontrar)
1.   Yo _____ a María.

2.   Felipe _____ a su novia.

3.   Nosotros _____ a unos amigos.

4.   Y tú, ¿a quién _____?

D.   (querer)
1.   Yo _____ ir al teatro.

2.   Mis primos _____ ir a la playa.

3.   Nosotros _____ ir al campo.

4.   Y tú, ¿qué _____ hacer?

E.   (dormir)
1.   Yo _____ mucho.

2.   Esteban _____ mal.

3.   Mis hermanos _____ poco.

4.   Nosotros _____ diez horas.

5.   Y tú, ¿_____ mucho o poco los domingos?

Test 6 Conversación   Complete the following conversations with the **yo** form of the underlined verbs.

1. —¿Conoces a María?

    —No, no la _____.

2. —¿Con quién sales el sábado próximo?

    —_____ con Carmen.

3. —¿Dónde pones los discos?

    —Los _____ en mi cuarto.

4. —¿Conduces el coche de tu papá?

    —No, no lo _____ nunca.

Test 7 Intérprete   Express the following sentences in Spanish.

1. *I never go to the theater.* _____

2. *I never listen to the radio.* _____

3. *What do you do on Sundays?* _____

4. *Do you work on Saturdays?* _____

5. *On Monday I am going to invite Carlos to the theater.* _____

6. *On Tuesday I am going to call Silvia.* _____

VOCABULARIO

Test 8 La palabra exacta   Of the two words in each set of parentheses, only one fits logically. Choose the word that fits and write it in the blank.

1. No _____ mi dinero. Lo ahorro.   (gano / gasto)

2. ¿Quién va a _____ el café? ¿Tú o yo?   (pagar / ahorrar)

3. Felipe le _____ el tocadiscos a Elena.   (pregunta / pide)

4. Te _____ cuándo vas al cine.   (pregunto / pido)

5. _____ es mi deporte favorito.   (La natación / El partido)

6. En un _____ de fútbol, hay once jugadores.   (aficionado / equipo)

7. _____ que la película es muy tonta.   (Pienso / Quiero)

8. El programa _____ a las diez.   (empieza / siente)

9. ¿_____ ir al teatro o al cine?   (Quieres / Entiendes)

10. ¿Cuánto _____ la Coca-Cola?   (cuenta / cuesta)

11. No me gusta _____ el tiempo.   (perder / encontrar)

12. Cuando estoy enfermo, _____ mal.   (recuerdo / duermo)

13. No _____ ayudarte porque no tengo tiempo.   (vuelvo / puedo)

14. Fernando no _____ a sus padres.   (obedece / pone) .

15. Carmen nos _____ los discos.   (sale / trae)

CULTURA

Test 9   ¿Sí o no?   Indicate whether the information in the statements below is true or false by circling **sí** or **no**.

sí   no   1. In Hispanic society, if a girl is invited by a boy to the movies she is expected to buy the tickets the next time they go out.

sí   no   2. In Spanish-speaking countries, married women are expected to work to earn money.

sí   no   3. The **peso** is used in different countries of Latin America.

sí   no   4. To promote tourism and international exchange, many Latin American countries have decided to adopt a unit of currency which has the same value in every country.

sí   no   5. **Fútbol** is the same game as our "football" in the U.S.

sí   no   6. **Fútbol** is the most popular sport in the Hispanic world.

sí   no   7. Although they like watching **fútbol** on TV, Hispanic teenagers usually do not play the game themselves.

sí   no   8. Hispanic teenagers enjoy movies very much.

sí   no   9. American movies are rarely shown in Spanish-speaking countries.

sí   no   10. Many Spanish-language movies are made in Spain, Argentina and Mexico.

sí   no   11. In Hispanic countries, parents usually let their daughters go to the movies alone or with a boy friend.

sí   no   12. Hispanic parents are much stricter with their sons than with their daughters.

UNIDAD 7

LECCIÓN 1 Modas para los jóvenes

A1. **¿Eres un(a) retratista talentoso(a)?** *(Are you a talented portrait artist?)*

Look at the portraits below and describe each person. At the end, try to guess each person's age. In the empty box, insert a portrait of your own: you may draw it, use a photograph, or cut a face out of a magazine. Describe that person also.

Adela

Carlos

Mona Lisa

➣ *Se llama Adela. Adela es delgada. Tiene el pelo rubio y liso. Tiene la nariz y la boca pequeñas y los ojos azules. Tiene doce años.*

1. _____

_____

_____

2. _____

_____

_____

3. _____

_____

_____

B1. **Las estrellas** *(The stars)*

Carmen, Marisela, and Luisa are the stars of the girls' volleyball team. Marisela is the captain. Compare her with the other two girls.

Carmen   Marisela   Luisa

➣ alto   *Marisela es menos alta que Carmen, pero más alta que Luisa.*

1. delgado _____

2. fuerte   _____

3. atlético _____

B2. Comparaciones

Compare the following things, places and people in terms of the adjectives in parentheses.

∽ un Mercedes / un Jaguar (rápido) *Un Mercedes es más (menos) rápido que un Jaguar. (Un Mercedes es tan rápido como un Jaguar.)*

1. el español / el inglés (difícil) _____

2. el tenis / el fútbol (interesante) _____

3. Nueva York / San Francisco (grande) _____

4. Robert Redford / John Travolta (guapo) _____

5. los chicos / las chicas (deportista) _____

C1. ¿Conoces bien tu ciudad?

How well do you know your city or neighborhood? What is the most expensive restaurant? Which are the cheapest stores? (If you don't know, guess.)

∽ el restaurante: caro *El restaurante más caro es Maxim's.*

1. el restaurante: barato _____
2. el restaurante: bueno _____
3. el hotel: moderno _____
4. el hotel: grande _____
5. la escuela: moderno _____
6. la escuela: bueno _____
7. las tiendas: elegante _____
8. las tiendas: barato _____

Las comparaciones

Answer the following questions in complete Spanish sentences.

1. *Do you have brothers and sisters?* _____
2. *Are they younger or older?* _____
3. *Are you taller than your best friend?* _____
4. *Are you younger or older?* _____
5. *According to you, who is the handsomest man in the world?* _____
6. *Who is the most beautiful woman?* _____
7. *Who is the most interesting person?* _____

LECCIÓN 2 La ropa es un problema

V1. Las banderas de los países hispánicos (*Flags of Hispanic countries*)

Color the flags below. Then write the colors of each. (You can find these flags in an encyclopedia or almanac.)

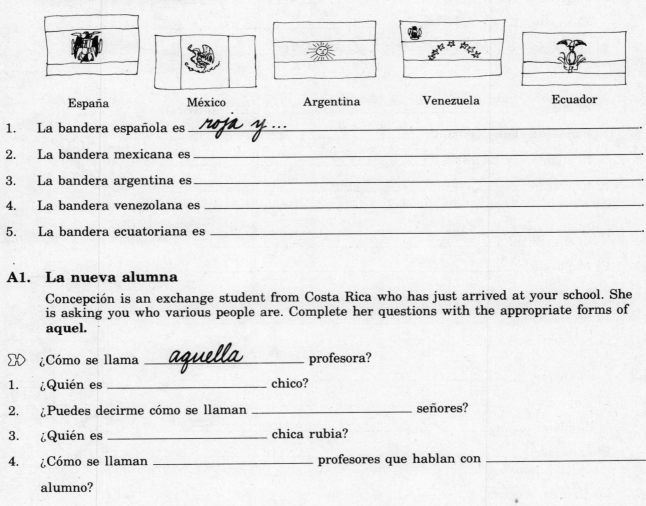

España   México   Argentina   Venezuela   Ecuador

1. La bandera española es _roja y..._ _____.

2. La bandera mexicana es _____.

3. La bandera argentina es_____.

4. La bandera venezolana es _____.

5. La bandera ecuatoriana es _____.

A1. La nueva alumna

Concepción is an exchange student from Costa Rica who has just arrived at your school. She is asking you who various people are. Complete her questions with the appropriate forms of **aquel.**

∑⟩ ¿Cómo se llama ____*aquella*____ profesora?

1. ¿Quién es _____ chico?

2. ¿Puedes decirme cómo se llaman _____ señores?

3. ¿Quién es _____ chica rubia?

4. ¿Cómo se llaman _____ profesores que hablan con _____

alumno?

B1. Preferencias

Imagine for a moment that you and your friends like different things. If your friends like one color, you like another. If they like things from one country, you prefer things from another. Use your imagination and complete the conversations according to the model.

∑⟩ Me gusta el suéter azul. _Prefiero el rojo (verde, amarillo...)._

∑⟩ Me gustan los coches japoneses. _Prefiero los italianos (franceses...)._

1. Me gustan los zapatos blancos. _____

2. Me gustan las chicas rubias. _____

3. Me gustan los pantalones azules. _____

4. Me gusta la literatura inglesa. _____

5. Me gusta la música puertorriqueña. _____

V2. De venta (On sale)

Everything is on sale at "Las Galerías Preciados," a large Spanish department store. Write the dialogs that take place between the salesperson (empleado) and the customer who wants to know the old and new prices.

El cliente: *¿Cuánto cuesta este libro?*

El empleado: *Por lo general, cuesta doscientas pesetas.*

El cliente: *¿Y ahora?*

El empleado: *Cuesta solamente sesenta.*

1. El cliente: _____ corbata?

   El empleado: Por lo general, _____

   El cliente: ¿Y ahora? _____

   El empleado: _____

2. El cliente: _____

   El empleado: _____

   El cliente: _____

   El empleado: _____

3. El cliente: _____

   El empleado: _____

   El cliente: _____

   El empleado: _____

¿Cuál ropa?

Answer the following questions in complete Spanish sentences.

1. *Do you wear blue jeans to school?* _____

2. *Do you buy your own clothes?* _____

3. *Do you have many sweaters?* _____

4. *What colors are they?* _____

5. *Do you wear glasses?* _____

6. *Do you wear sunglasses?* _____

7. *Are you going to buy a bathing suit this summer?* _____

LECCIÓN 3 ¡El pobre Sr. Ochoa!

A1. Antes del partido (*Before the game*)

Not everyone trains for the big game. Say who does and who does not, using the appropriate forms of **prepararse** (*to get ready*).

➣ Isabel (sí)   *Isabel se prepara.* _____

1. yo (sí)   _____

2. Carlos (no)   _____

3. tú (no)   _____

4. nosotros (sí)   _____

5. Felipe y Francisco (no) _____

6. Ud. (sí)   _____

7. Uds. (no)   _____

A2. De compras (*Shopping*)

revistas
50 pesetas

libros
150 pesetas

sandalias
425 pesetas

discos
250 pesetas

camisas
500 pesetas

anteojos de sol
300 pesetas

The following people are going shopping. Say what they buy for themselves with the money they have. (Of course, several purchases are possible. It is up to you to decide what each one wants to get.)

➣ Carlos tiene 500 pesetas. *Se compra dos discos (tres libros, una camisa, un libro y anteojos de sol, etc.).*

1. Felipe tiene 100 pesetas. _____

_____

2. Silvia y Carmen tienen 400 pesetas. _____

_____

3. Ud. tiene 250 pesetas. _____

_____

4. Uds. tienen 1.500 pesetas. _____

_____

5. Tenemos 1.000 pesetas. _____

6. Yo tengo 350 pesetas. _____

_____

7. Tú tienes 800 pesetas. _____

_____

B1. Después del partido de volibol

After the volleyball game the following people go home and do something different for themselves. Fill in the appropriate reflexive pronouns.

1. Felipe _____ lava.

2. Nosotros _____ bañamos.

3. Tú _____ haces un sándwich.

4. Yo _____ preparo un bistec *(steak)*.

5. Ud. _____ compra un kilo de chocolate.

6. Carmen y Cecilia _____ bañan.

B2. Cada mañana a las siete y media

Every day at 7:30, the following people do what they always do. Write each one's activities.

Carmen *se mira en el espejo* .

1. El Sr. Montero _____

2. Pedro y Paco _____

_____.

3. La Sra. de Vilas _____

_____.

¿Cómo te vistes?

Answer the following questions in complete Spanish sentences.

1. *What do you buy yourself with your money?* _____

_____

2. *What clothes do you put on when you go to a party?* _____

_____

3. *What clothes do you put on when you go to the beach?* _____

_____

4. *Do you dress well?* _____

5. *Do you often look at yourself in the mirror?* _____

_____

LECCIÓN 4   Una persona pulcra

A1. Los deportes

Say which parts of the body are used in the following sports.

↪ Para jugar al básquetbol, usamos *las manos*.

1. Para jugar al volibol, usamos _____.

2. Para nadar, usamos _____ y _____.

3. Para jugar a la pelota *(handball)*, usamos _____.

4. Un buen jugador de fútbol usa _____ y _____, pero no

    puede usar _____.

5. Tenemos dos manos: _____ izquierda y _____

    _____. En el béisbol, la mayoría de los lanzadores *(pitchers)* usan

    _____, pero algunos usan _____.

6. Para patinar *(skate)*, usamos _____.

B1. ¿A qué hora?

Not everyone has a nine-to-five job. Many people have jobs for which they get up very early or very late. In your opinion, at what time do the following people wake up and at what time do they go to bed? Use the appropriate forms of the verbs **despertarse** and **acostarse**.

↪ Carlos es guitarrista en un cabaret.

Se despierta a las dos de la tarde. Se acuesta a las seis de la mañana.

1. Elena es enfermera *(nurse)* de noche en un hospital.

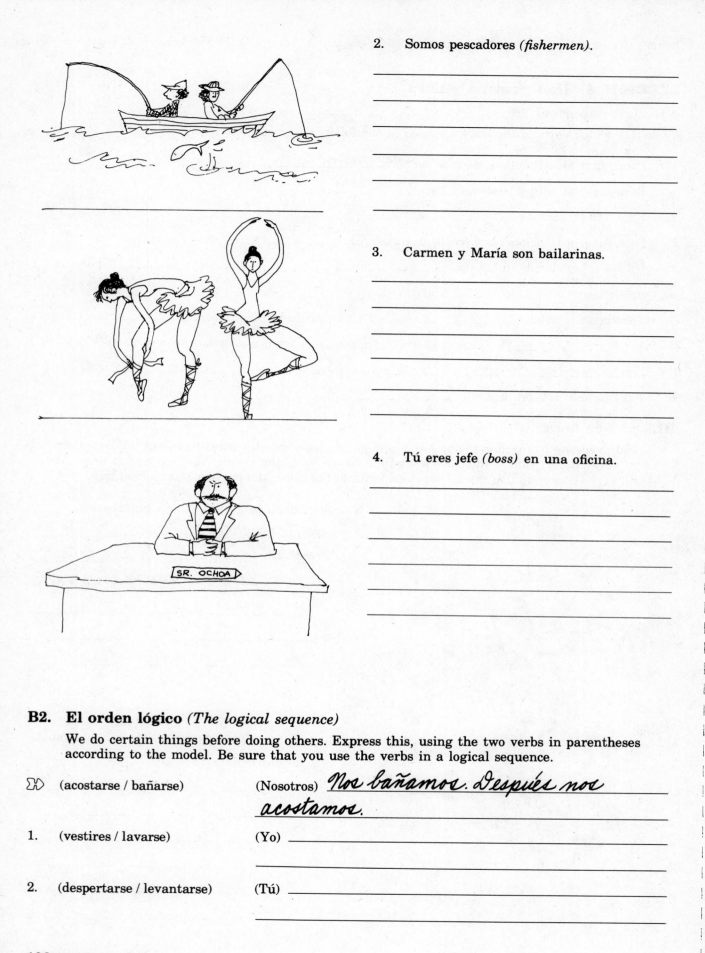

2. Somos pescadores (*fishermen*).

_____

_____

_____

_____

_____

3. Carmen y María son bailarinas.

_____

_____

_____

_____

_____

4. Tú eres jefe (*boss*) en una oficina.

_____

_____

_____

_____

_____

SR. OCHOA

B2. El orden lógico (*The logical sequence*)

We do certain things before doing others. Express this, using the two verbs in parentheses according to the model. Be sure that you use the verbs in a logical sequence.

Ↄ (acostarse / bañarse)   (Nosotros) *Nos bañamos. Después nos acostamos.*

1. (vestires / lavarse)   (Yo) _____

_____

2. (despertarse / levantarse)   (Tú) _____

_____

3.   (peinarse / bañarse)   Isabel _____

_____

4.   (lavarse / ponerse perfume)   La novia de Carlos _____

_____

B3.   Depende de la ocasión

Give logical completions for the following sentences. Use a reflexive verb of your choice. You may want to consider the following verbs: **acostarse / divertirse / dormirse / irse / quedarse / sentarse / sentirse / lavarse / bañarse / vestirse.**

⊠   Cuando la clase es aburrida, *me voy (me duermo, me siento de mal humor, etc.)* .

1.   Cuando veo una película tonta, _____

2.   Cuando estoy en una fiesta, _____

3.   Cuando estoy con personas simpáticas, _____

4.   Cuando tengo una cita, _____

5.   Después de jugar al fútbol, _____

6.   Cuando mis amigos están de mal humor, _____

7.   Cuando estoy enfermo(a), _____

B4. ¡Un poco de lógica, por favor!

What we do depends on how we're feeling. Express this, using elements A, B, C and D in affirmative or negative sentences according to the model.

A	B	C	D
sentirse	mal	ir a	acostarse
	bien	poder	sentarse
	de buen humor	tener que	divertirse
	contento		quedarse en casa
	cansado		quedarse en cama (bed)
	enfermo		irse al campo
			irse

♂ Carlos *(no) se siente bien. (No) va a acostarse.*

1. Felipe _____

2. Raúl y Carmen _____

3. Mis amigos _____

4. El profesor _____

5. Yo _____

6. Tú _____

7. Nosotros _____

Tus hábitos

Answer the following questions in complete Spanish sentences.

1. *Do you have fun in school?* _____

_____

2. *Do you have fun with your friends?* _____

_____

3. *At what time do you go to bed on Saturdays?* _____

_____

4. *At what time do you get up on Sundays?* _____

_____

5. *Do you stay home on Sundays?* _____

_____

El rincón cultural

El arte de la publicidad

Publicity is part of our life. We see it every day on TV, in newspapers, in the streets, on buses—and we hear it on the radio. A good ad must convey a simple and direct message to the person who reads it or hears it: Buy our product and use our services.

Look at these Spanish ads. They contain many words which you do not know. However, if they are good ads you should be able to understand their messages. Check how effective these are by answering the questions below.

This ad is announcing a special sale.

1. Which products are advertised? _____

2. How much do the blouses cost now? _____

3. How much did they cost before? _____

This ad advertises clothes for boys and girls to wear on graduation day. The first item advertised is the **guayabera**, a sports shirt which is popular in Hispanic countries.

4. Which country originated the style of the

    guayabera in the ad? _____

5. In which colors are they available?

    _____

6. What other items of clothing are advertised

    for boys? _____

7. What clothes are advertised for girls?

    _____

This ad has been placed by a flower shop.

8. How do you say "natural flowers" in Spanish? _____

9. The Spanish expression for "flower shop" is one word. Can you identify it? (Hint: it is derived from the Spanish word for flower.) _____

10. What is the name of the flower shop which placed the ad? _____

11. What kinds of flowers are mentioned in the ad? _____

_____

_____

_____

12. What type of product is advertised here? _____

13. How do you say "toothbrush" in Spanish? _____

14. What is the brand name of the toothbrush in the ad? _____

15. According to the ad, how many times a day should you use your toothbrush? _____

Enrich your vocabulary through Spanish   the Latin connection

Many of the words in this unit come directly from Latin. Many English words are related to these same Latin roots. Match the English words in parentheses with their corresponding definitions.

1. **estrecho** (from the Latin **strictus:** *tight, severe)*

   a.   a measure which severely narrows your options: a _____ measure

   b.   a person who is severe as a teacher is: _____

   c.   a snake which tightly holds its prey: a boa _____
   (constrictor   restrictive   strict)

2. **corto** (from the Latin **curtus:** *short)*

   a.   a very brief response: a _____ response

   b.   to cut short: to _____
   (curt   curtail)

3. **fuerte** (from the Latin **fortis:** *strong)*

   a.   a stronghold: a _____ or a _____

   b.   to strengthen: to _____

   c.   to console someone and give strength: to _____
   (comfort   fortification   fortify   fortress)

4. **débil** (from the Latin **debilis:** *weak)*

   a.   an illness which takes away your strength and leaves you weak:

   a _____ sickness

   b.   feebleness or weakness: _____

   c.   to weaken: to _____
   (debilitate   debilitating   debility)

5. **mejor** (from the Latin **melior:** *better)*

   a.   improved weather: an _____ in the weather

   b.   to improve or better one's behavior: to _____ one's behavior
   (ameliorate   amelioration)

6. **ojo** (from the Latin **oculus:** *eye)*

   a. an eye doctor: an _____

   b. field glasses designed to be used by both eyes at once: _____

   c. a reading lens for one eye: _____

   d. pertaining to the eye: _____

   (binoculars   monocle   ocular   oculist)

7. **cuerpo** (from the Latin **corpus:** *body)*

   a. bodily punishment: _____ punishment

   b. a dead body: a _____

   c. a person with a bulky body: a _____ person

   d. a small body or cell in the bloodstream: a white or red _____

   e. a body of persons under military command: a _____ of soldiers

   (corporal   corps   corpse   corpulent   corpuscle)

8. **pelo** (from the Latin **pilus:** *hair)*

   a. the skin of a fox with its hair: a _____

   b. a cream used for removing hair: a _____ cream

   (depilatory   pelt)

9. **pie** (from the Latin **pes:** *foot)*

   a. someone who walks or goes on foot: a _____

   b. an insect with 100 feet: a _____

   c. to have your toenails filed and polished: to have a _____

   d. a lever worked by the foot: a _____

   (centipede   pedal   pedestrian   pedicure)

10. **mano** (from the Latin **manus:** *hand)*

   a. a text written by hand: a _____

   b. to have your fingernails filed and polished: to have a _____

   c. to handle: to _____

   d. work done with one's hands: _____ labor

   e. handcuffs: _____

   (manacles   manage   manicure   manual   manuscript)

11. **vestirse** (from the Latin **vestire:** *to clothe)*

   a. ceremonial robes worn by a priest: _____

   b. to remove one's clothes or one's power: to _____

   c. the room in a church where ceremonial robes are kept: the _____

   (divest   vestments   vestry)

TEST / REPASO   Unidad 7

ESTRUCTURA

Test 1   Las comparaciones   Compare the four people below by completing the sentences with the missing words.

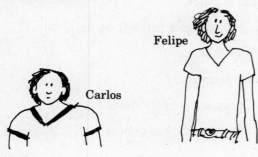

Felipe

Carlos

Enrique

Paco

1.   Felipe es _____ alto _____ Carlos.

2.   Carlos es _____ alto _____ Paco.

3.   Enrique es _____ alto _____ Paco.

4.   De los cuatro amigos, Felipe es _____ chico _____ alto.

5.   De los cuatro amigos, Paco es _____ chico _____ delgado.

Test 2   En el almacén grande *(At the department store)*   Sara taped conversations she overheard in a department store in Bogotá. Because of the noise, certain words were not very clear. Complete the transcript by filling in the blanks with the appropriate forms of the underlined words.

Estas sandalias cuestan mucho.

1.   No me gusta _____ disco.

2.   Quiero comprarme _____ libros.

3.   ¿Te gusta _____ bicicleta?

Esa bicicleta es inglesa.

4.   ¿Cuánto cuestan _____ cámaras?

5.   ¡Mira _____ televisor!

6.   _____ bolsos son bonitos, ¿verdad?

¡Escucha **aquellos** discos!

7.   ¿Por qué no compras _____ reloj?

8.   ¿Cuánto cuesta _____ revista?

9.   _____ cintas son muy baratas.

Test 3   El lanzamiento en paracaídas *(Parachute jumping)*   The following people are getting ready for their first parachute jump. Express this by completing the sentences below with the appropriate forms of the reflexive verb **prepararse.**

1.   Paco _____.

2.   Yo _____.

3.   Elena _____.

4.   Emilio y sus hermanos _____.

5.   Nosotros _____.

6.   Tú _____.

Test 4 Actividades   Roberto and his friends are doing various activities. Read each statement and decide whether the action is reflexive or not. Fill in the blanks with either the reflexive pronoun **se** or the suggested direct object pronoun.

✍ (Se / La) Roberto tiene una novia. _La_ invita al cine.

1. (Se / La) Carmen entra en el cuarto de baño. _____ lava.

2. (Se / Lo) Jaime tiene un coche. _____ lava todos los sábados.

3. (Se / Lo) Felipe quiere comprar el coche de Luis. _____ compra por mil dólares.

4. (Se / La) Inés necesita ropa nueva. _____ compra una falda azul.

5. (se / lo) Mañana hay un examen. El profesor _____ prepara.

6. (se / la) Hay una fiesta esta noche. Maribel _____ prepara para la fiesta.

7. (se / la) Para Gabriela la apariencia personal es muy importante. Esta chica _____ mira a menudo en el espejo.

8. (Se / La) Rafael quiere a Sofía. _____ mira a menudo.

Test 5 El fin de semana   Say who is going to stay home this weekend and who is not. Complete the sentences below with the appropriate forms of **ir a quedarse**.

✍ Elena no _va a quedarse_ en casa.

1. Mis primos _____ en casa.

2. Yo no _____ en casa.

3. ¿Y tú? ¿ _____ en casa?

4. Nosotros no _____ en casa.

5. Antonio _____ en casa.

Test 6 Intérprete   Provide the Spanish equivalents of the sentences below.

1. *Do you prefer the blue car or the red one?*

    _____

2. *I like the big house, but I prefer the small one.*

    _____

3. *I have black hair.*

    _____

4. *Elena has blue eyes.*

    _____

5. *Carlos washes his hands.*

    _____

6. *Josefina washes her hair.*

    _____

VOCABULARIO

Test 7 Un poco de anatomía   Write the names of the parts of the body corresponding to the numbers in the illustration. Be sure to use the appropriate forms of the <u>definite</u> article.

1. _____
2. _____
3. _____
4. _____
5. _____
6. _____
7. _____
8. _____
9. _____
10. _____

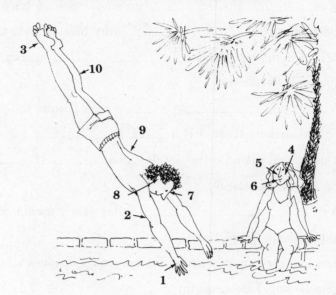

Test 8   Los sospechosos *(The suspects)*   As you hear the burglar alarm go off in the bank across the street, you see four people leaving the building and note how each one is dressed. Complete your written descriptions by filling in the items of clothing which correspond to each number.

A.   El hombre lleva un (1) _____ nuevo, un (2) _____ gris y

(3) _____ negros.

B.   La señora lleva (4) _____ de sol, un (5) _____ rojo y

(6) _____ amarillos.

C.   La muchacha lleva una (7) _____ verde, una (8) _____

azul y (9) _____ blancos.

D.   El muchacho lleva una (10) _____ blanca, una

(11) _____ roja y un (12) _____ negro.

Test 9   El verbo que conviene *(The suitable verb)*   Complete the sentences below by writing in the expression in parentheses which logically fits.

1. _____ en el cuarto de baño. (Me lavo / Me levanto)

2. Paco no necesita _____ porque tiene el pelo muy corto. (peinarse / ponerse)

3. Eva _____ un suéter porque hace mucho frío. (se pone / se quita)

4. Alberto _____ muy bien cuando tiene una cita con Olga. (se viste / se mira)

5. Mi hermano no quiere _____ cuando el agua *(water)* está fría.

   (bañarse / vestirse)

6. Voy a _____ en casa porque tengo que estudiar. (quedarme / irme)

7. Si comes demasiado, vas a _____ enfermo. (sentirte / sentarte)

8. Cuando mi mamá mira la televisión, _____ en ese sofá.

   (se sienta / se siente)

9. Voy a _____ a las seis y media porque mañana tengo una clase a las ocho.

   (levantarme / divertirme)

10. Los domingos por la noche leo un poco y después _____.

    (me levanto / me acuesto)

CULTURA

Test 10   ¿Sí o no?   Indicate whether the information contained in the statements below is true or false by circling **sí** or **no.**

sí   no   1. Hispanic teenagers pay attention to the way they look.

sí   no   2. Most Hispanic teenagers buy very expensive clothes.

sí   no   3. In Spanish-speaking countries, wearing flashy clothes is considered to be in poor taste.

sí   no   4. In Hispanic schools, the dress code is often stricter than in American schools.

sí   no   5. In Spanish-speaking countries, mothers often go with their daughters to buy clothing.

sí   no   6. Hispanic teenagers usually get a large allowance so that they can pay for their own clothing.

sí   no   7. Because they have few clothes, Hispanic teenagers go to parties in the same clothes they wear to school.

sí   no   8. If you plan to attend church in a Hispanic country, it is best to dress conservatively.

sí   no   9. There is a Spanish proverb which says: "If you are well dressed, you will be welcome everywhere."

sí   no   10. When Hispanic teenagers go to a public beach, they are not allowed to wear jeans.

UNIDAD 8

LECCIÓN 1   ¡Estas cosas ocurren siempre!

A1. ¡Celebraciones!

Certain occasions call for celebrations while others do not. Describe what has just happened to the people below and say whether or not they are going to celebrate.

⊗ Mi papá _*acaba de*_ comprar un coche nuevo. _*Va a celebrar.*_

1. Nosotros _____ perder el partido de fútbol. _____

2. Carmen _____ sacar una buena nota. _____

3. Mis amigos _____ ganar 100 dólares. _____

4. Tú _____ salir mal en el examen. _____

5. El Sr. y la Sra. de Álvarez _____ tener un bebé. _____

A2. Un poco de lógica

Imagine how the following people feel and find explanations for their feelings. Use elements of A, B, and C in logical sentences.

A	B		C	
contento	perder	recibir	el partido de tenis	una buena nota
enojado	ganar	encontrar	1.000 pesetas	un amigo
	sacar	pelear (to fight) con	una mala nota	buenas notas

⊗ Carlos _*está enojado porque acaba de pelear con un amigo*_

1. El equipo del colegio _____.

2. Mi tío _____.

3. Los alumnos _____.

4. Uds. _____.

5. Yo _____.

6. Tú _____.

B1. Los nuevos ciudadanos (The new citizens)

Say how long these people have been living in the U.S. Complete the sentences according to the model.

⊗ yo: 1 año _*Hace un año que vivo aquí.*_

1. Manuel: 20 años _____

2. el Sr. Abastado: 15 años _____

3. nosotros: 2 años _____

4. tú: 4 semanas _____

5. Felipe y Susana: 3 meses _____

B2. No más (No more)

Marisol finds out that many changes have taken place in the life of her friend Ana. Complete the dialogs between the two girls, using the expressions in parentheses.

Marisol:

Ana:

∑ (vivir: 3 meses)

¿No ___vives___ en Puerto Rico?   ¡No! *Hace 3 meses que vivo* en Nueva York.

1. (salir: 1 año)

¿No _____ con Juan?   ¡No! _____ con Alberto.

2. (trabajar: unas semanas)

¿No _____ como secretaria?   ¡No! _____ como fotógrafa.

3. (estudiar: 6 meses)

¿No _____ italiano?   ¡No! _____ francés.

4. (tener: 2 semanas)

¿No _____ el pelo castaño?   ¡No! _____ el pelo rubio.

B3. Un poco de historia

Answer the following questions in the affirmative, saying for how long the statements have been true. Give an approximate number of years. If you do not know, make a guess. Check your answers in an encyclopedia. Note: **unos** means *about* when it precedes a number.

∑ ¿Son los Estados Unidos un país independiente? *Sí, hace unos 200 años que los Estados Unidos son un país independiente.*

1. ¿Es México un país independiente? _____

_____

2. ¿Es el Nuevo México un estado? _____

_____

3. ¿Son los puertorriqueños ciudadanos (citizens) norteamericanos? _____

_____

¿Por cuánto tiempo?

Answer the following questions in complete Spanish sentences.

1. *How long have you been living in this city?* _____

_____

2. *How long have you been going to this school?* _____

_____

3. *How long have you been studying Spanish?* _____

_____

LECCIÓN 2   Un día que no empezó bien

A1.   El Rastro de Madrid

"El Rastro," in Madrid, is a large flea market where you can buy almost anything. Say what each of the following people bought and how much they paid. Use the preterite of **comprar** in the first sentence and the preterite of **gastar** in the second.

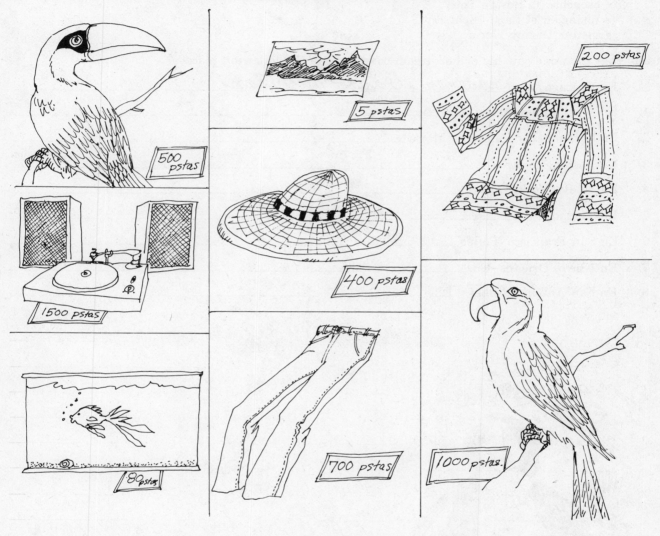

☞   Juan Carlos _*compró*_ 4 tarjetas. _*Gastó veinte pesetas.*_

1.   Pablo _____ 1 papagayo y 2 peces. _____

2.   Lidia y María _____ 1 tocadiscos muy viejo. _____

3.   Rafael y Andrés _____ 2 sombreros. _____

4.   Yo _____ blue-jeans. _____

5.   Tú _____ 1 camisa de Marruecos *(Morocco)*. _____

6.   Nosotros _____ 2 pájaros tropicales. _____

7.   Uds. _____ 1 sombrero y 1 camisa. _____

A2. La realización de los sueños *(Dreams coming true)*

A group of students visiting the United States have seen the following dreams come true:

- hablar con el presidente de los Estados Unidos
- sacar fotos de «El Álamo»
- admirar la Estatua de la Libertad
- escuchar jazz en el barrio francés
- visitar el barrio chino
- trabajar en un rancho
- escuchar la Boston Pops
- nadar en el Lago Michigan
- visitar Disney World

Say that each one saw his or her dream come true in the following places.

⊁ En Chicago, yo *nadé en el Lago Michigan* .

1. En Washington, María _____ .

2. En Orlando, los amigos de María _____ .

3. En Boston, nosotros _____ .

4. En Nueva York, Uds. _____ .

5. En Tucson, tú _____ .

6. En San Francisco, Felipe _____ .

7. En Nueva Orleans, Ud. _____ .

8. En San Antonio, Isabel y Elba _____ .

B1. Un día en la vida de Claudia Montoya

Claudia Montoya, a famous Spanish pop singer, leads a very busy life. Every night she writes down her plans for the next day. At the end of each day she calls her mother and tells her what she did. Read the entries in Claudia's notebook and complete the phone conversation she had with her mother the next evening. Use object pronouns in Claudia's answers.

por la mañana:
  pasar por la estación de servicio
  dejar el Rolls-Royce allí
  pagar el mecánico
  encontrar mi pasaporte nuevo
  pasar por la agencia de viajes
  encontrar el billete de avión para Nueva York

por la tarde:
  tocar la guitarra por dos horas
  empezar la grabación de mi disco nuevo «Mi Amor»
  llamar a Carmen
  jugar al tenis con ella

pasar por *drop by*   **billete** *ticket*   **grabación** *recording*

Sra. de Montoya: ¿Qué tal, Claudia?

    Claudia: Regular, mamá.

Sra. de M: ¿___*Pasaste*___ por la estación de servicio esta mañana?

    Claudia: Sí, _____.

Sra. de M: ¿_____ el Rolls-Royce?

    Claudia: Sí, _____.

Sra. de M: ¿_____ al mecánico?

    Claudia: _____.

Sra. de M: ¿_____ tu pasaporte nuevo?

    Claudia: _____.

Sra. de M: ¿_____ por la agencia de viajes?

    Claudia: _____.

Sra. de M: ¿_____ el billete de avión para Nueva York?

    Claudia: _____.

Sra. de M: ¿_____ la guitarra esa tarde?

    Claudia: _____ por _____.

Sra. de M: ¿_____ la grabación?

Claudia: _____.

Sra. de M: ¿_____ a Carmen por teléfono?

Claudia: _____.

Sra. de M: ¿_____ al tenis?

Claudia: _____ con _____.

Sra. de M: ¡Eres una chica muy ocupada!

Los incidentes

Relate five good things and five not-so-good things that have happened to you in the past five months. You may want to use the following verbs in affirmative or negative sentences: **invitar / comprar / jugar / dejar / pasar / equivocarse / mandar / prestar / quedarse / llamar / empezar / sacar.**

Cosas buenas:

⊗ *Un amigo me invitó a ir a un restaurante.*

1. _____
2. _____
3. _____
4. _____
5. _____

Cosas malas:

⊗ *Saqué malas notas en la clase de matemáticas.*

6. _____
7. _____
8. _____
9. _____
10. _____

LECCIÓN 3   ¡Qué suerte!

A1.   La fiesta mexicana

Last Saturday, students from the Mexican-American Alliance went out together. Say with whom the people below went out, using the preterite of **salir**.

➢ José (Susana) _José salió con Susana_____ .

1. Rebeca (Manuel) _____ .

2. Javier y Salvador (Rosa y Anita) _____ .

3. nosotras (unos chicos mexicanos) _____ .

4. tú (Andrea) _____ .

5. yo (Carmen) _____ .

A2.   Pérdidas y ganancias *(Profit and loss)*

The following people went to Spain on vacation. They bought several items that they later sold to their friends. Say how much money each one gained or lost. Use the preterite forms of **comprar, vender, ganar** and **perder**.

➢ (un reloj: 20/15)   Rafael _compró un reloj por veinte dólares. Lo vendió por quince. Perdió cinco dólares._

1. (una guitarra: 30/60)   Mis primos _____
_____

2. (un sombrero andaluz: 35/15)   Yo _____
_____

3. (unos discos flamencos: 10/15)   Nosotros _____
_____

4. (un bolso: 25/5)   Carmen _____
_____

C1.   ¡Acusaciones!

When Tomás returned to his apartment, he noticed that some destructive friends had been there in his absence. He wants to know who is responsible for the mess he finds. Complete his questions with the appropriate forms of the verbs in parentheses.

➢ (romper) ¿Quién _rompió_____ el tocadiscos?

1. (romper) ¿Quién _____ el radio?

2. (escribir) ¿Quién _____ tonterías *(foolish things)* en mi cuaderno?

3. (leer) ¿Quién _____ mi correspondencia?

4. (descubrir) ¿Quién _____ mi diario?

5. (dar) ¿Quién le _____ el bistec *(steak)* al gato?

C2. La casa encantada (The haunted house)

On a dare, a group of friends decided to go into a haunted house. Say what strange things they saw and heard, using the preterite of **ver** and **oír** and the words in parentheses.

    ∽ (algo / nada)   Pedro   *vio algo. No oyó nada.*

1. (nada / algo)   Tú _____

2. (algo / algo)   Nosotros _____

3. (nada / nada)   Tomás _____

4. (algo / nada)   Yo _____

5. (nada / algo)   Mis hermanos _____

C3. El robo (The burglary)

Carmen is a witness to a bank robbery. This is what she notes down while the burglary is taking place:

Oigo un ruido en la calle San Martín. Miro y veo un coche con tres hombres enmascarados. El conductor se queda en el coche mientras los otros entran en el banco. Cinco minutos después, salen del banco con un saco muy grande. El conductor los ayuda a poner el saco en el coche. Salen muy de prisa.

enmascarados *masked*   **conductor** *driver*   **mientras** *while*   **saco** *bag*   **muy de prisa** *very quickly*

One hour later Carmen was at the police station where she told what she saw. Write her testimony, using the preterite.

Oí un ruido en la calle San Martín.

_____

_____

_____

_____

_____

Una página de un diario

From now on you should try to keep a diary in Spanish in which you note the main events of the day. Start your diary today by writing a short paragraph using eight of the following verbs: **levantarse / tomar / estudiar / invitar / dar / beber / ayudar / comer / comprar / escribir / aprender / ver / asistir / salir.**

_____

_____

_____

_____

_____

LECCIÓN 4   Noticias de todos los días

A1.   El viaje de Isabel

Isabel spent a month in Spain last summer.
Describe the things she did in each city where
she went, using the **yo** form of the preterite of
the verbs in parentheses. Be careful: the verbs
are not necessarily given in the order in which
you have to use them.

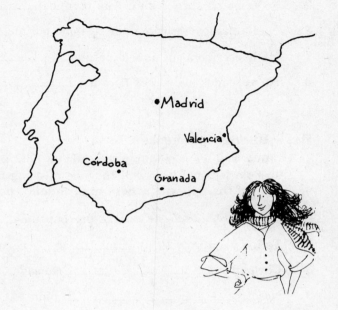

1. en Madrid: (visitar / sacar / llegar)

   *Llegué*_____ a Madrid el 2 de julio.

   _____ el famoso museo del Prado.

   _____ muchas fotos de la capital.

2. en Valencia: (comer / nadar / encontrar)

   _____ a mi amiga Luisa.

   _____ en el mar Mediterráneo.

   _____ la famosa paella valenciana.

3. en Granada: (salir / ver / escuchar)

   _____ la Alhambra.

   _____ con un amigo español.

   _____ la música flamenca.

4. en Córdoba: (asistir / comprar / aprender)

   _____ sandalias.

   _____ a una corrida.

   _____ a tocar la guitarra.

A2.   Excusas

There is always a reason why some students have not studied for an exam. Find a different
excuse for each of the students listed, using **prepararse** and elements of A and B in logical
sentences.

A		B	
perder	vender	el brazo	en la escalera (*stairway*)
olvidar	ayudar	el libro	la fecha del examen
romperse	visitar	a un amigo	el cuaderno
caer		a un vecino (*neighbor*) enfermo	

∞ Carlos *no se preparó para el examen porque perdió el libro*_____.

1. Carmen _____.

2. Nosotros _____.

3. Yo _____.

4. Tú _____.

5. Francisco y Pepe _____.

A3. ¡Basta! *(That's enough!)*

The following people are not doing certain things because they did them yesterday. Express this by completing the sentences with the appropriate preterite forms of the verbs given.

☞ No juego al fútbol porque ___*jugué ayer*___.

1. Carlos y Jaime no juegan al tenis porque _____

2. Federico no encuentra a Ana porque _____

3. No llamamos a Susana por teléfono porque _____

4. No le escribo a mi abuelo porque _____

5. No aprendes los verbos porque _____

B1. ¡Buenas noches!

How well we sleep often depends on how we felt during the day. Describe how the following people felt and how well they slept, using the preterite forms of **sentirse** and **dormir** plus one of the following: **bien, mal, mucho, poco.**

☞ Yo ___*me sentí*___ preocupado. ___*Dormí poco.*___

1. Felipe y Luis _____ nerviosos. _____

2. Carmen _____ cansada. _____

3. Nosotros _____ bien. _____

4. Tú _____ mal. _____

5. Yo _____ enfermo. _____

V1. Un poco de lógica

Complete the following sentences logically, using an expression with **tener.**

☞ Voy a acostarme porque ___*tengo sueño*___.

1. Vamos al restaurante porque _____

2. Carmen se quita la chaqueta porque _____

3. Javier se pone un suéter y un abrigo porque _____

4. Voy a tomar una Coca-Cola porque _____

El diario

Describe some of the things you did yesterday by answering the following questions in Spanish, using complete sentences.

1. *At what time did you wake up?* _____

2. *What did you eat for lunch?* _____

3. *What did you drink?* _____

4. *What time did you go to bed?* _____

5. *Did you sleep well?* _____

Nombre _____ Fecha _____

El rincón cultural
Restaurantes

```
SÁNDWICHES              AERORESTAURANTE            JUGOS

De jamón        $ 23,00      MENU                  De piña          $ 12,00
De queso          23,00                            De tomate          15,00
Combinados        23,00                            De potes           15,00
De carne          23,00   HUEVOS Y TORTILLAS       FUENTE DE SODA     Zapote con leche   12,00
De pollo          23,00                                               Tajadas de papaya  12,00
"Colombia"        70,00   Huevos al gusto  $ 20,00  Milo con leche  $ 12,00  Tajadas de piña  12,00
Hamburguesas      23,00   Huevos con jamón   40,00  Chocolate con leche  10,00  Limón natural  12,00
Perro Caliente    20,00   Tortilla con pollo 80,00  Café con leche   5,00  Tajadas de Melón  12,00
Hamburguesa Especial 35,00  " con camarines  80,00  Leche fría o caliente  5,00  Otras gaseosas   4,00
                          " con jamón        80,00  Tinto o aromáticas   2,00
```

This **Aerorestaurante** is located in the airport at Bogotá, the capital of Colombia. It offers many of the same foods and drinks that one would find in most international airports.

Imagine that you have spent your vacation in Colombia with other American students. Now you are at the airport waiting for your return flight to the United States. Since you and your friends are a little hungry, you have gone to the **Aerorestaurante.**

Look at the menu. You can probably identify many of the items listed. Here is a brief glossary which will help you to select what you want:

la carne	*meat*	un huevo	*egg*	una piña	*pineapple*	caliente	*hot*
el jamón	*ham*	una tortilla	*omelet*	el pollo	*chicken*	una tajada	*slice*

You are going to order for everyone. Ask the waiter for the following items by completing the sentence as indicated.

Por favor, ¿puede Ud. traernos . . .

(2 eggs with ham)   *dos huevos con jamón* ,

(1 cheese sandwich) _____ ,

(1 chicken sandwich) _____ ,

(1 ham omelet) _____ ,

(3 hamburgers) _____ ,

(2 hot dogs) _____ ,

(2 coffees, with milk) _____ , y

(2 slices of pineapple) _____ ? ¡Muchas gracias!

Now you are going to order for yourself and a friend. Imagine that you have only 135 pesos (or about $4.00). From the menu select four items, one from each of the following categories. Be sure that the total does not exceed 135 pesos.

A. jugo o fruta _____ $_____

B. sándwich _____ _____

C. huevos y tortillas _____ _____

D. fuente de soda _____ _____

La cuenta

When you have finished your meal, the **camarero** (*waiter*) will bring you **la cuenta** (*the bill*). The illustration shows the bill from a Spanish restaurant called **La Alegría**.

Los restaurantes hispánicos en los Estados Unidos

Is Hispanic food always hot and spicy? If you answered yes, you are probably thinking of Mexican food. In reality, there are many styles of Hispanic cooking. Typical foods vary from country to country, and within a country each region has its own specialties.

Obviously you do not have to leave the United States to sample Hispanic food. There are many Hispanic restaurants in this country, especially in the Southwest, in California, in Florida, and in the larger cities. The four restaurants whose advertisements you see below are located in New York. Note that each one specializes in a particular type of cooking.

Enrich your vocabulary through Spanish   the Latin connection

The following Spanish words from this unit are derived from Latin. There are many English words which have the same Latin roots. Match the English words in parentheses with their corresponding definitions.

1. **agua** (from the Latin **aqua:** *water)*

    a.   a plant which grows in the water: an _____ plant

    b.   a tank filled with water: an _____

    c.   a system which brings water to the city: an _____

    d.   a plane which can land on the water: an _____
          (aquaplane   aquarium   aquatic   aqueduct)

2. **fin** (from the Latin **finis:** *end)*

    a.   an exam given at the end of the term: a _____ exam

    b.   the concluding part of a musical composition: the _____

    c.   contestants chosen towards the end of a competition: _____

    d.   to bring to completion: to _____
          (final   finale   finalists   finalize)

3. **vino** (from the Latin **vinum:** *wine)*

    a.   sour wine: _____

    b.   the plant on which grapes are grown to produce wine: _____

    c.   a good year for wine: a _____ year

    d.   a person who makes wine: a _____
          (vine   vinegar   vintage   vintner)

4. **fácil** (from the Latin **facilis:** *easy, done with ease)*

    a.   to make someone's task easier: to _____ the task

    b.   to play the piano with ease: to play with _____

    c.   a solution achieved with ease: a _____ solution
          (facile   facilitate   facility)

5. **feliz** (from the Latin **felix:** *happy)*

    a.   great happiness: _____

    b.   a happy and appropriate choice: a _____ choice

    c.   to congratulate on a happy occasion: to _____
          (felicitate   felicitous   felicity)

6. **deber** (from the Latin **debere:** *to owe; to be obliged to*)

   a. a person who owes money: a _____

   b. the money that is owed: the _____

   c. to be obligated to or to owe someone: to be _____ to that person

   (debt   debtor   indebted)

7. **equivocarse** (from the Latin **aequivocus:** *having a double meaning*)

   a. an answer which is unclear: an _____ answer

   b. a very clear decision: an _____ decision

   c. to speak unclearly, with ambiguities: to _____

   (equivocal   equivocate   unequivocal)

8. **romper** (from the Latin **rumpere:** *to break*)

   a. an appendix which has burst: a _____ appendix

   b. to break in when someone is speaking: to _____

   c. to disturb a class: to _____ a class

   d. the bursting forth of a volcano: a volcanic _____

   (disrupt   eruption   interrupt   ruptured)

TEST / REPASO Unidad 8

ESTRUCTURA

Test 1 En la fiesta   Everyone danced at the party last night. Say who danced with whom by completing the sentences below with the preterite of **bailar.**

1. Carlos _____ con Isabel.

2. Mis primas _____ con un estudiante español.

3. Nosotros _____ con Elena y Adela.

4. Yo _____ con Ramón.

5. Tú _____ con Susana.

6. Ud. _____ con la profesora.

7. Uds. _____ con sus amigas.

8. Rafael y yo _____ con nuestras novias.

Test 2 Ayer y hoy   We often do the same things more than once, but we do them differently. Say what the following people did yesterday by completing the sentences with the appropriate forms of the underlined verbs.

Hoy:

Ayer:

⇒ Paco <u>come</u> en la cafetería.

_____*Comió*_____ en un restaurante francés.

1. <u>Hablas</u> con el profesor de inglés.

_____ con la profesora de español.

2. <u>Trabajamos</u> mucho.

_____ poco.

3. Héctor y Luis <u>tocan</u> el piano.

_____ la guitarra.

4. <u>Invito</u> a Susana al cine.

_____ a Amalia.

5. <u>Como</u> con mis padres.

_____ con mi novia.

6. <u>Recibo</u> una buena nota.

_____ una mala nota.

7. <u>Comes</u> un pastel.

_____ un helado.

8. Le <u>escribes</u> a tu prima.

Le _____ a tu abuela.

9. El gato <u>rompe</u> un vaso.

_____ un plato.

10. Rafael no <u>comprende</u> la lección.

No _____ las preguntas.

11. <u>Bebemos</u> Coca-Cola.

_____ gaseosas.

12. <u>Recibimos</u> un telegrama.

_____ una carta.

13. Mis primos <u>venden</u> su tocadiscos.

_____ sus discos.

14. Luisa y Bárbara <u>reciben</u> un regalo.

_____ dinero.

Test 3 Raúl y Ramón   Whatever Raúl does, Ramón did a few weeks ago. Complete Ramón's statements by filling in the **yo** forms of the preterite of the underlined verbs.

Raúl: Ramón:

1. <u>Toco</u> el piano.   Yo también _____ el piano.

2. <u>Saco</u> buenas notas.   Yo también _____ buenas notas.

3. <u>Llego</u> tarde al colegio.   Yo también _____ tarde.

4. <u>Organizo</u> una fiesta.   Yo también _____ una fiesta.

5. <u>Encuentro</u> a Ana.   Yo también la _____.

6. <u>Pienso</u> en el futuro.   Yo también _____ en el futuro.

7. Me <u>siento</u> muy feliz.   Yo también me _____ muy feliz.

8. <u>Empiezo</u> una novela muy interesante.   Yo también _____ una novela.

9. <u>Juego</u> al tenis con Isabel.   Yo también _____ con ella.

10. <u>Veo</u> a Teresa.   Yo también la _____.

11. Le <u>doy</u> a mi mamá un regalo.   Yo también le _____ un regalo a mi mamá.

Test 4 Intérprete   Give the Spanish equivalents of the following sentences.

1. *I have just spoken with Ana.* _____

2. *Emilio has just gone to the movies.* _____

3. *We have just seen Enrique.* _____

4. *I have been living in San Juan for one year.* _____

_____

5. *Clara has been working here for one month.* _____

_____

6. *We have been studying Spanish for six months.* _____

_____

VOCABULARIO

Test 5 En el restaurante   Imagine that you are working in a Spanish restaurant. Offer your customers a logical choice between items on the menu by completing the missing words.

    ➢ ¿Quiere Ud. té o c *a f é* ?

1. ¿Quiere Ud. leche o a ___ ___ ___ ?

2. ¿Quiere Ud. un sándwich o una h ___ ___ ___ ___ ___ ___ ___ ___ ___ ___ ___ ?

3. ¿Quiere Ud. un pastel o un h ___ ___ ___ ___ ?

4. ¿Quiere Ud. vino o c ___ ___ ___ ___ ___ ?

5. ¿Quiere Ud. jugo de frutas o una g ___ ___ ___ ___ ___ ?

Test 6 La lógica   Complete the following sentences with the word in parentheses which logically fits.

1. Si no estudias, vas a sacar una mala _____.   (nota / tarea)

2. El español es un idioma _____: millones de personas lo hablan.   (útil / inútil)

3. Soy perfecto. No me _____ nunca.   (equivoco / divierto)

4. Puedes _____ tus libros aquí.   (pasar / dejar)

5. ¿Dónde vas a _____ las vacaciones?   (cambiar / pasar)

6. ¡Dios mío! _____ a qué hora es el examen.   (Me olvidé / Dejé)

7. Vamos a ir al cine _____.   (anoche / esta noche)

8. ¿Cuándo hablaste con Pedro? ¿_____, o el sábado pasado?   (Ayer / Mañana)

9. Paco siempre se levanta _____. ¡Hoy, se levantó a las seis!   (tarde / temprano)

10. ¿Quién _____ América?   (descubrió / recibió)

11. Un buen hijo _____ ayudar a sus padres.   (deja / debe)

12. No puedo jugar con Uds. porque _____ la pierna.   (me rompí / perdí)

13. Voy a dormir. ¡Tengo _____!   (hambre / sueño)

14. Si tienes _____, puedes beber agua.   (sed / frío)

CULTURA

Test 7 **¿Sí o no?**   Indicate whether the information contained in the following statements is correct or not by circling **sí** or **no.**

sí   no   1. South America is a continent in which the weather is always hot and humid.

sí   no   2. In Chile and Argentina, July and August are winter months.

sí   no   3. There are few Spanish-speaking ski champions because there are no snow-covered mountains in Spain and South America.

sí   no   4. School discipline is usually stricter in Hispanic countries than in the United States.

sí   no   5. In Hispanic countries, students are allowed to arrive at school late since it is not considered important to be on time.

sí   no   6. In Spanish-speaking countries, the 15th birthday is a very important celebration for both boys and girls.

sí   no   7. On her 15th birthday, a girl's godparents will give her a special gift.

sí   no   8. When a girl is 15, her parents often organize a big party in her honor.

sí   no   9. Spain is divided into 50 political provinces.

sí   no   10. A **Catalán** is a Spaniard who has emigrated to South America.

sí   no   11. Although Spain is one country, each region has maintained its own special character.

sí   no   12. The inhabitants of Spain identify both with their country and with their region of origin.

UNIDAD 9

LECCIÓN 1   ¿Tienes las habilidades necesarias?

A1.   ¿Los conocen?

Do you know the following people? Of course you do, even though you may not know them personally. Say that you know them and tell something that you know about them.

↬   tus vecinos *(neighbors)*   *Los conozco. Sé que se llaman Martino (que son italianos, que tienen un Ford, etc.).*

1.   el (la) director(a) del colegio _____

_____

2.   el (la) secretario(a) de la escuela _____

_____

3.   el (la) doctor(a) _____

_____

4.   el presidente de los Estados Unidos _____

_____

5.   Mohamed Alí _____

_____

6.   los Beatles _____

_____

A2.   ¿Tienen los requisitos? *(Do they have the qualifications?)*

Imagine that you are the director of a school of music and fine arts. When candidates come to see you, you ask whether they are properly qualified. Write your questions, using the appropriate form of **saber** and one of the following expressions: **cantar** / **dibujar** / **sacar fotos** / **actuar** *(to act)* / **bailar** / **tocar la guitarra** / **tocar el piano.**

los estudiantes:

el (la) director(a):

↬   Luis quiere ser guitarrista.   *¿Sabes tocar la guitarra?*

1.   Carlota quiere ser bailarina. _____

2.   Felipe quiere ser fotógrafo. _____

3.   Queremos ser dibujantes. _____

4.   Ricardo y Raúl quieren ser pianistas. _____

5.   Elena y María quieren ser actrices. _____

6.   Quiero ser cantante. _____

A3. El (la) periodista *(The journalist)*

Imagine that you are covering the Olympic Games. You want to write an article about the Spanish riding champion Miguel Arruza. Prepare the questions which you will ask a friend of his. Begin the sentences below with **Conoce Ud.** or **Sabe Ud.**, as appropriate.

1. ¿_____ bien a Carlos Arruza?

2. ¿_____ de dónde es?

3. ¿_____ cuántos años tiene?

4. ¿_____ si tiene novia?

5. ¿_____ a su novia?

B1. El secreto

María and Felipe have decided to elope. Say who knows the secret and who does not.

⋙ la mamá de María (sí) *Lo sabe.*_____

1. el papá de María (no) _____

2. los padres de Felipe (no) _____

3. yo (sí) _____

4. tú (no) _____

5. nosotros (sí) _____

B2. ¡No!

Carlos is in a very negative mood today and answers no to all of his brother Felipe's questions. Write out Carlos' answers.

⋙ Felipe: ¿Sabes dónde está Clara?

Carlos: *No lo sé.*_____

1. Felipe: ¿Sabes si Enrique va a ir al cine con nosotros?

Carlos: _____

2. Felipe: ¿Sabes si José quiere ir a la fiesta?

Carlos: _____

3. Felipe: ¿Sabes por qué estás de mal humor?

Carlos: _____

¿Qué sabes hacer?

Let's talk about your qualifications. Answer the questions below in complete Spanish sentences.

1. *Do you know how to type?* _____

2. *Do you know how to draw?* _____

3. *Do you want to be a doctor?* _____

4. *Do you want to be a social worker?* _____

LECCIÓN 2   Aspiraciones profesionales

A1.   Escuelas profesionales

For certain professions there are specific things one learns. Express this, using elements of columns A, B, and C in logical sentences.

A	B	C
desear	mecánico	sacar fotos
querer	enfermero(a)	dibujar
esperar	dibujante	reparar coches
pensar en	periodista	atender a los clientes
	fotógrafo(a)	escribir artículos
	aeromozo(a)	atender a los pasajeros (passengers)
	intérprete	cuidar a los enfermos (take care of sick people)
		hablar inglés y francés

⤳ Claudia *desea ser enfermera. Aprende a cuidar a los enfermos.*

1. Nosotros _____

2. Felipe y Miguel _____

3. Susana _____

4. Mis primos _____

5. Tú _____

B1.   Yo

Express your own wishes, projects and ambitions by completing the sentences below with a personal statement.

1. Quiero _____

2. Espero _____

3. Necesito _____

4. Quiero aprender a _____

5. Pienso en _____

6. En casa, trato de _____

7. En clase, trato de _____

8. Con mis amigos, trato de _____

9. Antes de graduarme del colegio, _____

10. Después de graduarme, _____

11. Estudio español para _____

12. Quiero ir a la universidad para _____

(En vez de ir a la universidad, pienso _____

13. Antes de casarme, _____

(En vez de casarme, _____

B2. Antes y después

There is a certain logic in what we do. For instance, we have to do certain things before we can do others. Express this according to the model. Be sure to maintain a logical sequence of events.

✷ lavar los platos *(plates)* / lavarse las manos

Pablo come.

Antes de comer, se lava las manos.
Después de comer, lava los platos.

1. ponerse pantalones viejos / lavarse las manos

    Isabel repara su bicicleta.

2. quitarse los pijamas / vestirse

    Nos bañamos.

3. pagarla / comparar los precios *(prices)*

    Mi papá escoge *(chooses)* una refrigeradora.

4. estar muy cansada / comprar una raqueta

    Mi prima juega al tenis.

B3. Lo contrario *(The opposite)*

The following people are doing the opposite of what they are supposed to do. Express this according to the model.

⮞ (dormir) Carlos no estudia. *En vez de estudiar, Carlos duerme.*

1. (mirar la televisión) Felipe no duerme. _____

2. (leer una novela de aventuras) No aprendemos los verbos. _____

3. (tocar la guitarra) Mis primos no trabajan. _____

4. (escribir a tu novia) No te preparas para el examen. _____

C1. Objetivos profesionales *(Professional goals)*

People choose their professions for individual reasons. Explain the choices of the people below by using elements of A and B in logical sentences.

A		B
abogado(a)	policía	ayudar a los otros
doctor(a)	dentista	ganar mucho dinero
vendedor(a)	trabajador(a) social	viajar
viajero(a)	profesor(a)	conocer a personas interesantes
aeromozo(a)		tener muchas vacaciones

⮞ Elena *quiere ser profesora para tener muchas vacaciones* _____

1. Yo _____
2. Tú _____
3. Nosotros _____
4. Mis primos _____
5. Carlos _____
6. Ud. _____
7. Uds. _____

C2. Los regalos

Santa Claus has brought the following gifts, but they have no labels. Distribute them to the persons listed.

unos discos / unos libros / una cámara / una raqueta / una caja *(box)* **de chocolates / un pasaporte**

∞ A Elena le gusta la música. *Los discos son para ella.*

1. A mí me gusta leer. _____

2. A mi papá le gusta sacar fotos. _____

3. A mis hermanos les gusta comer dulces *(candy)*. _____

4. A ti te gusta jugar al tenis. _____

5. A Ud. le gusta viajar. _____

Entrevista

Answer the following questions in complete Spanish sentences.

1. *Do you know how to drive?* _____

2. *Are you learning to drive?* _____

3. *Are you learning to play the guitar?* _____

4. *Are you beginning to speak Spanish well?* _____

5. *Do you sometimes forget to study?* _____

6. *Do you need to sleep a lot?* _____

LECCIÓN 3 Un trabajo de verano en España

A1. ¿Adónde fueron?

A group of young people are talking about their vacations. Can you guess to which of the following countries each one went?

España / el Canadá / Alemania *(Germany)* **/ Egipto / los Estados Unidos / Portugal**

⋙ Elba sacó fotos de la Plaza Mayor en Madrid. _*Fue a España.*_

1. Carlos asistió a un partido de fútbol americano. _____

2. José Antonio y Carmen vieron las pirámides muy altas y muy antiguas. _____

3. Visitamos Quebec. _____

4. Hablaste portugués. _____

5. Mis amigos visitaron Munich y Berlín. _____

B1. El secreto de todo el mundo

Carmen told Pedro a secret and asked him not to repeat it to anyone, but Pedro passed the secret on to his friends. Say how the secret made the rounds, using the appropriate preterite forms of **decir**.

1. Carmen le _____ un secreto a Pedro.

2. Pedro les _____ el secreto a sus amigos.

3. Los amigos de Pedro nos _____ el secreto a nosotros.

4. Nosotros te _____ el secreto de Carmen.

5. Tú me _____ el secreto.

6. Y yo le _____ el secreto a Carmen.

C1. Intercambios *(Exchanges)*

Imagine that you own the following items:

You want to acquire these items from your friends:

Propose some exchanges to your friends.

⋙ _¿Quieres cambiar tu pez por mi pájaro?_ _____

1. _____

2. _____

3. _____

4. _____

C2. Un viaje por Europa

Imagine that you have won a trip through Europe. You can visit as many countries as you like as long as your trip does not exceed six weeks (42 days). You have decided you want to see the following countries:
España / Portugal / Francia / Italia / Alemania / Grecia.

Plan your entire trip so as to meet the conditions of the prize.

➤ *Voy a viajar por España por siete días...*

1. _____

2. _____

3. _____

4. _____

5. _____

6. _____

Una solicitud de empleo *(An employment application)*

Imagine that you are spending a year in Spain. You are looking for a job. In a newspaper you have seen this "help wanted" ad. You feel that you are qualified. Write a letter of application.

> **Club Internacional de Vacaciones**
> busca a estudiantes bilingües
> — inglés y español —
> para ser guías turísticos
>
> Los candidatos deben . . .
> — ser de nacionalidad inglesa o norteamericana
> — tener excelente presentación
> — saber conducir
> — saber hablar en público
>
> Para más información, escribir al Sr. Roberto Ruiz / avenida José Antonio 72 / Madrid

Estimado Sr. Ruiz:
    Leí su anuncio y estoy muy interesado(a) en su oferta de trabajo.

                    Atentamente,

LECCIÓN 4   ¿Cuál es su trabajo?

A1.   Bromas malas *(Bad jokes)*

The following people have played bad jokes on their friends. They put the wrong things in the wrong places. Describe each bad joke by completing the sentences with the appropriate preterite forms of **poner**.

1. Enrique _____ la sal *(salt)* en el café.

2. Nosotros _____ la mostaza *(mustard)* en los pasteles.

3. Yo _____ el azúcar *(sugar)* en las hamburguesas.

4. Felipe y Carmen _____ el agua en el vino de su papá.

5. Tú _____ el vinagre en el helado.

6. Uds. _____ la mayonesa en la leche de Rosita.

A2.   Excusas, excusas

Very few people came to the Humphrey Bogart movie shown by the English club. Those who did not had something else to do. Invent an excuse for each of the following people.

⋑ Ramón   *no vino. Tuvo que ayudar a su mamá.* _____

1. Ana María _____

2. Yo _____

3. Los hermanos de Carlos _____

4. Tú _____

A3.   Una persona reticente

A bank robbery took place yesterday. The police suspect Ramón Hernández and are interrogating his girl friend Carmen Pereda, but Carmen is not very cooperative. Complete the dialog between Carmen and the detective by using the appropriate preterite forms of the verbs in parentheses.

⋑ (estar)

Detective: ¿ *Estuvo* _____ Ud. con Ramón Hernández ayer por la tarde?

Carmen: ¡No! *No estuve* _____ con él.

1. (ir)

Detective: Pués, ¿adónde _____ Ud.?

Carmen: _____ a casa.

2. (hacer)

Detective: ¿Y qué _____ Ud. allí?

Carmen: No _____ nada.

3. (venir)

Detective: ¿_____ Ramón Hernández a su casa?

Carmen: Sí, _____ por un momento.

4. (decir)

Detective: ¿Y qué le _____ Ud. a él?

Carmen: ¿Yo? No le _____ nada.

5. (poner)

Detective: ¿Sabe Ud. dónde _____ Ramón el dinero?

Carmen: No comprendo su pregunta.

B1. ¡Yo!

Do we do what we want to do? That depends on the circumstances. Express what you do according to the model.

↭ (hacer / querer)

En casa *(no) hago generalmente lo que quiero* _____.

1. (decir / pensar)

Con mi familia _____.

Con mi mejor amigo _____.

2. (comprender / aprender)

En la clase de español _____.

En la clase de matemáticas _____.

3. (encontrar / buscar)

En casa _____.

En la vida *(life)* _____.

4. (creer / leer)

En los periódicos _____.

En las novelas _____.

5. (creer / oír)

En la escuela _____.

En la radio _____.

El pasado

Answer the following questions in complete Spanish sentences.

1. *Did you do your homework yesterday?*

_____

2. *Did you take a trip during the vacation?*

_____

3. *Were you able to watch TV last night?*

_____

El rincón cultural

Ofertas de empleo

One day you may be living in a Spanish-speaking country and find that you are looking for a job. In that case, you would consult the employment ads in the local newspaper.

Here are several job offers which have recently appeared in Spanish newspapers and magazines. Although you may not understand every word, you should be able to get the basic meaning of each ad. Read each ad and try to answer the corresponding questions.

1. What job is offered? _____
   _____

2. What type of company (empresa) is looking
   for an employee? _____
   _____

3. Where is the job located? _____

4. What are the work hours? _____

IMPORTANTE EMPRESA INTERNACIONAL EN VILLAVERDE ALTO (MADRID - 21)
NECESITA
SECRETARIA BILINGÜE
ESPAÑOL - INGLES
para el director gerente
Horas de trabajo de 8 a 17.35. De lunes a viernes. Sábados libres
SUELDO A CONVENIR
Interesadas escribir a la ref. M-366.054.
General Pardiñas. 5. Madrid-1

5. What type of job is offered? _____
   _____

6. Does the company want a man or a
   woman? _____

7. Does the person need a car? _____

RELACIONES PUBLICAS
SE SOLICITA SEÑORITA
RELACIONES PUBLICAS
para importante empresa de Barcelona. Inteligente, hábil, conversadora, con carnet de conducir y vehículo propio Relacionada con el ramo de la publicidad o periodismo
Escribir a: **EDICIONES E. G. CURT, Vía Augusta, 108, Barcelona-6,** indicando experiencia y pretensiones. (BM-772.)

CHRYSLER ESPAÑA S.A.
precisa
TRADUCTORES TECNICOS

SE REQUIERE:
- Perfecto dominio del idioma inglés.
- Formación a nivel de Bachiller Superior.
- Mecanografía.
- Incorporación inmediata.

SE OFRECE:
- Jornada laboral de 8,30 a 17,30 horas.
- Comedor de empresa.
- Interesantes condiciones económicas.

Interesados envíen «curriculum vitae» a la Oficina de Colocación, General Pardiñas, 5, Madrid.
Referencia M-364.524
(M-364.524)

8. What is the name of the company placing the ad?
   _____

9. Where is the company located? _____

10. What types of openings are available? _____
    _____

11. Which languages are required? _____

12. How long is the working day? _____

13. What type of openings are available?

_____

14. Is the company looking for men, women,

or both? _____

15. What does the company sell? _____

16. Where is the job located? _____

_____

17. How many employees does this company

want to hire? _____

18. What type of job is offered?

_____

19. Are the jobs temporary or permanent?

_____

20. What is the minimum weekly salary?

_____

La escuela comercial

Look at the ad. It advertises courses at a commercial school.

21. What is the name of the school?

_____

_____

22. Where is the school located?

_____

23. What types of courses are offered?

_____

_____

24. When do the courses begin?

_____

Enrich your vocabulary through Spanish the Latin connection

Many of the names of professions you learned in this unit are not only derived from Latin, but are directly related in meaning and spelling to their English equivalents. Others are less directly related to English words, but come to us via Latin. Match the English words in parentheses with their corresponding definitions.

1. **abogado** (from the Latin **advocatus:** *lawyer, one who speaks out*)

   a. one who calls for justice: an _____ of justice

   b. to speak in support of reforms: to _____ reforms

   c. organ of speech: _____ chords

   d. one who speaks very loudly: a _____ person
      (advocate   advocate   vocal   vociferous)

2. **dentista** (from the Latin **dens:** *tooth)*

   a. false teeth: _____

   b. a flower whose name means "lion's tooth": _____

   c. toothpaste: _____
      (dandelion   dentifrice   dentures)

3. **locutor** (from the Latin **loqutor:** *one who speaks)*

   a. a person who speaks well: an _____ person

   b. the art of speaking well: the art of _____

   c. speech lessons: _____ lessons

   d. talkative: _____

   e. a speech by one person: a _____

   f. one who speaks from the stomach and projects his/her voice:

      a _____
      (elocution   eloquence   eloquent   loquacious   monologue   ventriloquist)

4. **modista** (from the Latin **modus:** *manner)*

   a. a manner of doing things: a _____ of doing things

   b. fashionable, in an up-to-date manner: _____

   c. clothes which are not in the manner of the day: clothes which are

      _____

   d. to change in keeping with the style of the day: to _____
      (mode   modernize   modish   outmoded)

Some of the Spanish prepositions you have learned in this unit come directly from Latin, and many English words include these same Latin roots as part of their meaning. Match the English words in parentheses with their corresponding definitions.

5. **sin** (from the Latin **sine:** *without)*

    a.   one who is without a mate: a _____ person

    b.   a job without any real duties: a _____

    c.   unique, without a like kind: _____
                             (sinecure   singular   single)

6. **antes** (from the Latin **ante:** *before, in front of)*

    a.   to be of an earlier date: to _____

    b.   money bet before cards are laid down, in a card game: an _____

    c.   one's ancestors; those who lived earlier: _____

    d.   a room where you wait before entering another: an _____
                  (ante   antecedents   antechamber   antedate)

7. **por** (from the Latin **per:** *through)*

    a.   to browse or read through something: to _____

    b.   capable of being soaked through: _____

    c.   to walk or stroll through an area: to _____
               (perambulate   peruse   permeable)

TEST / REPASO   Unidad 9

ESTRUCTURA

Test 1   En el club deportivo   The following people are active in a sports club. Tell what everyone is doing by filling in the blanks with **a** or **de** as needed. (If no word is required, write a dash in the blank.)

∞ Marta puede _____ jugar al volibol.

1. Sofía aprende _____ esquiar.

2. Antonio quiere _____ jugar al tenis.

3. Roberto deja _____ nadar porque está muy cansado.

4. Anita empieza _____ nadar muy bien.

5. Alberto trata _____ nadar cinco millas.

6. Luisa viene _____ jugar al tenis.

7. Felipe va _____ jugar al fútbol.

8. Inés espera _____ jugar con el equipo de básquetbol.

Test 2   El fin de semana pasado   Describe what the following people did last weekend by completing the sentences with the appropriate preterite forms of **ir**.

1. Carlos y yo _____ a una fiesta.

2. Manuel _____ al campo.

3. Tú _____ al cine.

4. Mi hermana _____ a la playa con su novio.

5. Yo _____ a bailar en la discoteca.

6. Ramón y sus primos _____ al centro.

7. Uds. _____ de compras (shopping).

8. Ud. _____ a un concierto.

Test 3   Lo que me gusta   Ana says that during the summer she did what she likes doing. Complete Ana's sentences with the **yo** form of the preterite of the underlined verbs.

1. Me gusta <u>conducir</u> coches rápidos.   El verano pasado, _____ un Jaguar.

2. Me gusta <u>traer</u> ropa nueva a la playa.   _____ mi traje de baño nuevo.

3. Me gusta <u>decir</u> la verdad.   Le _____ la verdad a Teresa.

4. Me gusta <u>hacer</u> viajes.   _____ un viaje al Uruguay.

5. Me gusta <u>estar</u> con mis amigos.   _____ con mis amigos.

6. Me gusta <u>poner</u> mi dinero en el banco.   _____ mi dinero en el banco.

7. Me gusta <u>saber</u> la verdad.   _____ la verdad.

8. Me gusta <u>poder</u> salir.   _____ salir.

Test 4 La estación de tren en Madrid   While waiting for her train in Madrid, Anita taped the conversation around her. Because of the noise, certain words are hard to understand. Complete each sentence with **por** or **para,** as appropriate.

1. ¿Cuál es el tren _____ Barcelona?

2. ¡Me gusta viajar _____ tren!

3. ¿Cuánto pagaste _____ esa revista?

4. ¿Trabaja Ud. _____ una agencia de viajes?

5. ¿Es ese telegrama _____ mí?

6. Quiero mandar esta carta _____ avión.

7. Tengo que llamar a mis primas _____ teléfono.

8. Si Ud. pasa _____ Granada, tiene que visitar la Alhambra.

9. Voy a París _____ aprender francés.

10. Y tú, vas a Francia _____ ganar dinero.

11. Voy a trabajar allí _____ un año.

12. Mi hermana trabaja _____ la IBM.

Test 5 Preguntas   There are many things that Paco wants to ask his friend Luisa, who is visiting him. Begin Paco's questions with **Sabes** or **Conoces,** as appropriate.

1. ¿_____ a mi prima?

2. ¿_____ que es ingeniera?

3. ¿_____ Madrid bien?

4. ¿_____ que hay muchos restaurantes buenos?

5. ¿_____ el restaurante «Sol Azteca»?

6. ¿_____ el Palacio Real?

7. ¿_____ a qué colegio asisto?

8. ¿_____ cómo se llama mi mejor amigo?

9. ¿_____ a la hermana de mi mejor amigo?

10. ¿_____ dónde vive?

Test 6 Intérprete   Give the Spanish equivalents of the following sentences.

1. *I work to earn money.* _____

2. *Do you study Spanish to go to Spain?* _____

   _____

3. *Before going to Paris, I want to* _____

   learn French. _____

4. *I am going to visit Mexico after* _____

   visiting Guatemala. _____

5. *I do not understand what you are saying.* _____

6. *Do you believe what I say?* _____

7. *I go to the movies from time to time.* _____

8. *Last month, I went to the movies twice.* _____

   _____

9. *How many times did you go to the movies?* _____

   _____

VOCABULARIO

Test 7 Un trabajo para cada uno   Match the people below with their jobs. To do this, write down the letter of the phrase which describes the work of each of the following.

  el fotógrafo ___D___   A.   ayuda a las familias pobres

1. el secretario _____   B.   repara los coches

2. la empleada _____   C.   tiene un barco

3. la aeromoza _____   D.   saca fotos

4. el enfermero _____   E.   acompaña a los turistas a los monumentos

5. el programador _____   F.   hace ropa para señoras

6. la trabajadora social _____   G.   dibuja planos

7. el guía _____   H.   trabaja en un hospital

8. la locutora _____   I.   va al aeropuerto

9. el dibujante _____   J.   vende libros y discos

10. la modista _____   K.   habla en la radio

11. el pescador _____   L.   trabaja con una computadora

12. el mecánico _____   M.   escribe a máquina

CULTURA

Test 8 ¿Sí o no?   Indicate whether the information contained in the statements below is true or false by circling **sí** or **no.**

sí   no   1. There are millions of people of Hispanic origin in the United States.

sí   no   2. Spanish is a useful language to know because it is spoken by many people.

sí   no   3. Knowing Spanish may give you an advantage in looking for a job, especially if you live in an area where there are Spanish speakers.

sí   no   4. In Hispanic countries, most families have two cars.

sí   no   5. Hispanic teenagers are good drivers because they own cars at a very early age.

sí   no   6. Tourists find Spain an attractive country.

sí   no   7. There are few beaches in Spain because there is little coastline.

sí   no   8. A **modista** is a person who designs men's clothes.

sí   no   9. Many Hispanic girls sew their own clothes.

sí   no   10. Sewing machines are so expensive in Latin America that very few families have one.

UNIDAD 10
LECCIÓN 1   Una receta del Caribe: refresco de plátanos
A1.   Durante las vacaciones

To keep in touch during vacation, we write or phone our friends. Say whether or not you usually keep in touch with the following people when you are away on vacation.

		llamar:	escribir:
⮑	mis profesores	*(No) los llamo.*	*(No) les escribo a ellos.*
1.	mis primos	_____	_____
2.	mi mejor amigo	_____	_____
3.	mi mejor amiga	_____	_____
4.	mis abuelos	_____	_____
5.	los alumnos de la clase de español	_____	_____

B1.   ¡Qué problemas!

Imagine that your friends have the following problems. Give each one appropriate advice using one or two of the following verbs with **más** or **menos**: **estudiar / trabajar / comer / leer / gastar / jugar / ahorrar / dormir / nadar.**

Tus amigos: Tú:

⮑ Silvia: Estoy muy cansada.   *Duerme más. Juega menos.*

1. Roberto: Estoy un poco gordo.   _____

2. Miguel: Estoy muy flaco.   _____

3. Susana: Quiero ser más delgada.   _____

4. Alberto: Tengo dolor de cabeza (*headache*).   _____

5. Carmen: Saco malas notas.   _____

6. Isabel: Al fin de la semana, no tengo dinero.   _____

7. Felipe: Quiero aprender muchas cosas interesantes.   _____

8. Raúl: Quiero ganar más dinero.   _____

9. Anita: Necesito más ejercicio físico.   _____

10. Alfonso: Mis amigos piensan que soy un estudiante demasiado serio.   _____

C1. El campamento de veraneo (Summer camp)

Imagine you are a counselor in a summer camp. Some of the children in your cabin need a little discipline. Tell them what to do.

⇒ Enrique no se levanta.   _¡Levántate, Enrique!_

1. Manuel no se acuesta. _____

2. Federico no se lava. _____

3. Paco no se queda en el dormitorio. _____

4. Miguel no se divierte. _____

C2. Unos consejos buenos

A friend asks your advice about what to do in certain situations. For each situation he mentions, give three suggestions using the following expressions. Be sure to use the appropriate pronouns in preparing your advice.

- ayudar
- escribir
- invitar
- visitar
- llamar por teléfono
- mandar una tarjeta
- comprar un regalo
- mandar un regalo
- traer flores
- traer una caja (box) de chocolates

Los problemas de tu amigo:

⇒ Mañana es el cumpleaños de mi primo, pero no puedo ir a la fiesta.

1. Mi mejor amigo está de mal humor (in a bad mood).

2. Mi prima va a casarse (to get married).

3. Las hijas de los vecinos están enfermas.

Tus consejos:

Llámalo por teléfono. Mándale una tarjeta. Mándale un regalo.

_____

_____

_____

_____

V1. Los utensilios necesarios

Say which utensils the following people need.

⇒ Elena va a beber una gaseosa.   _Necesita un vaso._

1. Voy a comer un bistec (steak). _____

2. Queremos comer pasteles. _____

3. Mis padres toman vino. _____

Tus relaciones con los otros

Answer the following questions in complete Spanish sentences, using only pronouns in your answers.

1. *Do you often help your friends?* _____

2. *Do you often write your cousins?* _____

3. *Do you know your teachers well?* _____

LECCIÓN 2   El A-B-C de la salud

V1.   En el restaurante

You are the chef in a new restaurant. Prepare the menu for the day.

Carnes: ___*pollo*___   Postres: _____

_____   _____

_____   _____

Vegetales: _____   Bebidas: _____

_____   _____

_____   _____

A1.   Excesos *(Overdoing it)*

The following people tend to overdo things. Suggest that they cut down on what they do.
(Note: **tanto** = *so much.*)

∞ Mi papá fuma *(smokes)* demasiado.   *¡No fumes tanto, Papá!* _____

1.   Carmen habla demasiado.   _____

2.   Ramón come demasiado.   _____

3.   Alberto bebe demasiado.   _____

4.   María Luisa trabaja demasiado.   _____

5.   Enrique estudia demasiado.   _____

6.   Elvira lee demasiado.   _____

7.   Elba duerme demasiado.   _____

A2.   Cambios *(Changes)*

Your friends tell you what they do. Suggest that they do other things.

∞ Aprendo francés.   *No aprendas francés. Aprende* _____ español.

1.   Como carne.   _____ vegetales.

2.   Tomo gaseosas.   _____ agua.

3.   Escucho música popular. _____ música clásica.

4.   Compro cosas inútiles.   _____ cosas útiles.

5.   Leo historietas *(comics)*. _____ novelas.

6.   Pido dinero.   _____ consejos.

B1. Invitaciones

Imagine that a friend is asking you whether or not to invite the following people to a party. Give your opinion in the affirmative or negative.

Tu amigo:	Tú:
✺ Pedro es aburrido.	¡ *No lo invites* !
1. Alberto es muy divertido.	
2. Inés y Teresa tocan la guitarra muy bien.	
3. Mis primas dicen mentiras *(lies)*.	
4. Isabel compró discos nuevos ayer.	

B2. El coche deportivo *(The sports car)*

Today you are trying out your new sports car and you have asked your friend to go with you on a picnic. Your friend asks whether she can bring along the following. Answer her—but remember that the car is only a two-seater. Use affirmative or negative forms of **traer.**

Tu amiga:	Tú:
✺ ¿Traigo mi tocadiscos?	¡ *No lo traigas* !
1. ¿Traigo mi guitarra?	
2. ¿Traigo mi cámara?	
3. ¿Traigo mis anteojos de sol?	
4. ¿Traigo mi perro?	

B3. El sarampión *(Measles)*

Your little sister has a bad case of measles. The doctor has ordered that she not get out of bed for at least two days. She asks you whether or not she can do the following things. Answer her appropriately.

Tu hermana:	Tú:
✺ ¿Me quedo en casa?	*Sí, ¡ quédate en casa!*
1. ¿Me quedo en cama?	
2. ¿Me baño?	
3. ¿Me siento en el sofá?	
4. ¿Me duermo?	

La comida y tú

Answer the following questions in complete Spanish sentences.

1. *What type of meat do you like?* _____

_____

2. *Which vegetables don't you like?* _____

_____

3. *What is your favorite dessert?* _____

_____

LECCIÓN 3 ¡Bravo, Sra. de Ortiz!

A1. Música

A friend of yours has brought over some records for you to listen to. Tell him which ones you want him to play. Use affirmative or negative commands with **poner** and the appropriate pronouns.

✍ un disco de Bob Dylan   *¡ Ponlo! (¡ No lo pongas !)* _____

1. una sinfonía clásica   _____

2. un concierto de piano   _____

3. un disco de Barbra Streisand   _____

4. un disco de los Beatles   _____

5. unos discos de música popular   _____

6. unos discos de jazz   _____

B1. Consejos buenos

Give a friend some good advice. To do this, use the verb in parentheses in affirmative and negative sentences.

1. (decir)   ¡_____ la verdad!

    ¡_____ mentiras!

2. (hacer)   ¡_____ la tarea!

    ¡_____ cosas tontas!

3. (dar)   ¡_____ *les* consejos buenos a tus amigos!

    ¡_____ les _____ consejos malos!

4. (estar)   ¡_____ de buen humor!

    ¡_____ de mal humor!

5. (ser)   ¡_____ generoso(a)!

    ¡_____ intolerante!

6. (ir)   ¡_____ a la escuela!

    ¡_____ a la playa si tienes que estudiar!

7. (poner)   ¡_____ tu ropa en el armario *(closet)*!

    ¡_____ los zapatos en la mesa!

8. (salir)   ¡_____ con chicos simpáticos!

    ¡_____ con chicos antipáticos!

C1. Tus posesiones personales

Tell who bought the following items for you, or whether you bought them for yourself.

↝ tu reloj *Mi mamá me lo compró. (Yo me lo compré.)*

1. tu radio _____

2. tus discos _____

3. tus libros _____

4. tu ropa _____

C2. ¡No!

We don't always get what we ask for. Complete the dialogs below according to the model, using the verbs in parentheses and the appropriate pronouns.

↝ (prestar)

Luis: ¿ *Me prestas* tus libros de inglés?

Carmen: *No, no te los presto.*

Luis: *¿Por qué no quieres prestármelos?*

Carmen: *Porque los* necesito.

1. (dar)

Carlos: ¿_____ tu foto?

Teresa: _____

Carlos: _____

Teresa: ¡_____ perdí!

2. (comprar)

Marisol: Mamá, ¿_____ aquella falda?

La Sra. de Ochoa: _____

Marisol: _____

La Sra. de Ochoa: _____ encuentro demasiada corta.

3. (enseñar)

Emilio: ¿_____ tus revistas?

Pedro: _____

Emilio: _____

Pedro: _____ necesito.

LECCIÓN 4   Una conspiración

A1.   Prudencia *(Caution)*

Imagine that a friend has asked you to lend him the following items. Since you know that he never returns anything, you reply that you do not have them any more. Then say what you did with them, using the verbs in parentheses.

El amigo: Tú:

∿   ¿Me prestas tu bicicleta?   *Ya no la tengo.*

(prestar) *Se la presté* a Manuel.

1.   ¿Me prestas tus discos?   _____

(prestar) _____ a los chicos españoles.

2.   ¿Me prestas tus revistas?   _____

(mandar) _____ a la chica francesa.

3.   ¿Me prestas tu lámpara?   _____

(dar) _____ a Carmen.

4.   ¿Me prestas tus notas?   _____

(mandar) _____ a mi compañero de clase.

5.   ¿Me prestas tu guitarra?   _____

(dar) _____ a mi hermana.

B1.   Los invitados *(Guests)*

Juan has invited five people to his birthday dinner. Study the seating arrangement and describe where each person is seated in relation to the others.

∿   María está   *al lado de*   Manuel y   *a la derecha de*   Rubén.

1.   Carmen está _____ Juan y _____ Manuel.

2.   Isabel está _____ Juan y _____ Rubén.

3.   Manuel está _____ María y _____ Carmen.

B2. Un lugar para todo

Imagine that you have rented the apartment illustrated here and that you have bought the following pieces of furniture. Say where you will place each piece. Be very specific, indicating your plans according to the model. Use the prepositions you have learned in this lesson.

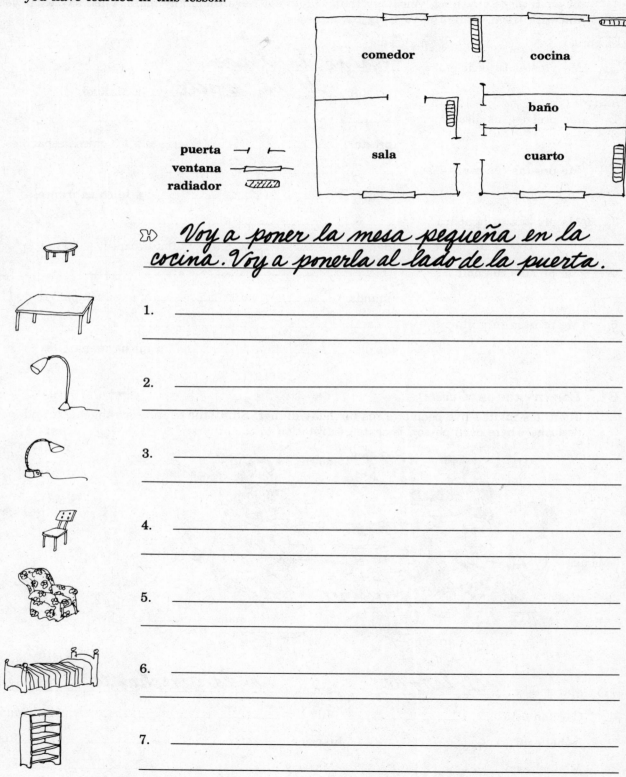

comedor	cocina
	baño
sala	cuarto

puerta ⊣ ⊢
ventana ▭
radiador ▱

» *Voy a poner la mesa pequeña en la cocina. Voy a ponerla al lado de la puerta.*

1. _____

2. _____

3. _____

4. _____

5. _____

6. _____

7. _____

El rincón cultural

Una guía de salud (A health guide)

Good eating habits include a balanced diet and an adequate calorie intake. This table gives the caloric values of various foods. Remember that most Spanish speakers use the metric system: 100 grams equals about 3½ ounces.

Alimentos	Calorias	Alimentos	Calorias
Legumbres y vegetales		**Quesos y huevos**	
una zanahoria	20	un huevo	80
un tomate	20	queso suizo (una tajada)°	90
una papa	80	queso norteamericano (una tajada)	80
cinco hojas° de lechuga	10		
Frutas		**Pan, cereales y espaguetis**	
un plátano	90	una taza de «Corn Flakes»	100
una naranja	70	una taza de espagueti	150
una manzana	70	pan (una rebanada)	70
Carnes		**Bebidas**	
un bistec (100 gramos)	230	un vaso de leche	160
pollo (100 gramos)	200	un vaso de jugo de tomates	50
jamón (100 gramos)	240	un vaso de jugo de naranja	100
Postres		un vaso de gaseosa	100
helado (media taza)	200	una taza de té o café	0
pastel (una rebanada)°	250		
chocolate (una barra)	200		

hoja leaf   **rebanada** slice   **tajada** slice

Now add up the caloric intake of the three meals described below:

Desayuno: dos huevos _____

pan tostado

un vaso de jugo de naranja _____

una taza de té _____

total: _____

Almuerzo: un bistec de 150 gramos _____

dos papas

lechuga _____

dos tajadas de queso suizo _____

dos rebanadas de pan _____

una naranja _____

un vaso de leche _____

total: _____

Cena: sándwich de jamón _____

pollo con espagueti _____

lechuga

helado _____

café _____

total: _____

Una Guia Para Comer Bien

Consuma Diariamente:

Leche y sus Productos

3 o más vasos de leche—Ninos
vasos más chicos para algunos ninos menores de 8 anos

4 o más vasos—Jóvenes

2 o más vasos—Adultos

Queso, helado o mantecado y otros alimentos hechos con leche pueden suplir parte de la leche

2 o más porciones

Carnes, ave y pescado, huevos o queso —con frijoles secos, alverjas y nueces, como suplentes

Grupo de Carnes

Vegetales y Frutas

4 o más porciones

Incluya vegetales verdes o amarillos; frutas citrosas o tomates

4 o más porciones

Enriquecidos con vitaminas o de grano entero. Con la leche se aumenta su valor alimenticio

Panes y Cereales

Nuestra dieta

The amount of calories a person needs every day depends on several factors: age, sex and activity. Imagine that you are working as a dietician. Prepare the menus for the following two people so that each one obtains the right amount of calories and the right balance of foods according to the **Guía.**

a) Roberto is 18 years old and works as a mechanic. He requires 3500 calories per day.
b) La Sra. de Móntez is 40 years old and overweight. Her doctor told her to reduce her intake to 1800 calories per day.

las comidas de Roberto

desayuno: _____

_____

_____

almuerzo: _____

_____

_____

cena: _____

_____

_____

total: _____

las comidas de la Sra. de Móntez

desayuno: _____

_____

_____

almuerzo: _____

_____

_____

cena: _____

_____

_____

total: _____

Enrich your vocabulary through Spanish   the Arabic connection

A little bit of history   Did you know that the word "orange" comes from Arabic? As a matter of fact, the English language contains many common words of Arabic origin. Why is this? Again, let us turn to the history of Spain.

At the beginning of the seventh century A.D. a new religion appeared in the Middle East. This religion, Islam, was founded by Mohammed (570-632), a well-to-do Arab merchant born in Mecca. The success of Islam, the Moslem religion, was phenomenal. Less than one hundred years after Mohammed's death it had spread across the entire Arabian peninsula into Persia, Turkestan, Egypt and North Africa. In 711 an army of Moors, an Arabic tribe from North Africa, crossed the Straits of Gibraltar and invaded Spain.

The Moors were to occupy most of Spain for nearly eight centuries, bringing with them a sophisticated civilization. Learning and culture flourished in Islamic Spain, especially around Toledo, Granada, Córdoba and Sevilla. This period witnessed great achievements in architecture, medicine, mathematics, chemistry, philosophy and literature.

However, the Moors did not impose their religion on the Spanish people, who remained Christians. Little by little the Christian princes reconquered Spain, until the last Moslem king was defeated in 1492 (the year Columbus landed in America!).

The Moslems departed from Spain, but left behind many reminders of their 800-year occupation. The Spanish language, for example, absorbed many Arabic words which subsequently passed into other European languages such as French, Italian and English.

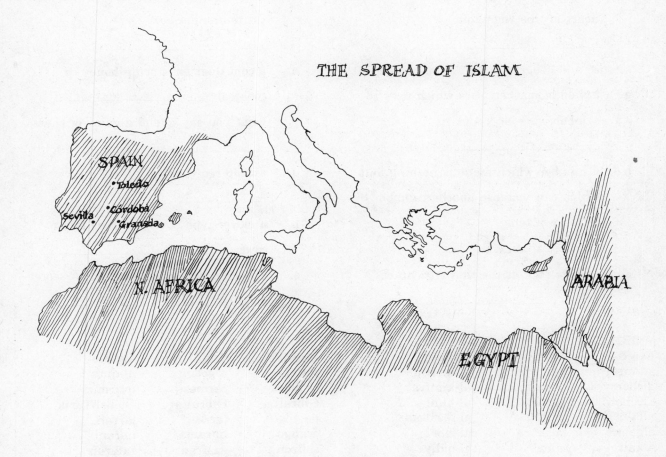

THE SPREAD OF ISLAM

SPAIN
Toledo
Sevilla   Córdoba
Granada
N. AFRICA
ARABIA
EGYPT

Arabic words in English

The English words defined below are of Arabic origin. Can you identify them? To help you, these words are listed alphabetically at the bottom of the page with their Spanish and Arabic equivalents.

1. foods

   a. a tropical fruit which grows in Florida and California:

   _____

   b. a product used to sweeten tea and coffee: _____

   c. a reddish-yellow fruit which may be eaten dry: _____

   d. a substance found in wine, beer and whisky: _____

   e. a yellow spice used in oriental cooking: _____

   f. you nibble the leaves and eat the heart of this vegetable:

   _____

2. science and geography

   g. a field of mathematics which uses symbols such as x and y:

   _____

   h. a number which alone is nothing, but which can increase another number by a factor of ten:

   _____

   i. a large rock at the southern tip of Spain: _____

   j. a chemical base which may contain potassium or sodium:

   _____

   k. a medieval science whose aim was to transform lead into gold:

   _____

   l. the highest point in the sky:

   _____

3. other words

   m. the top rank in the navy:

   _____

   n. a natural textile used in making shirts and dresses:

   _____

   o. a container for storing honey or cookies: _____

   p. what you say to end a game of chess:

   _____

   q. a deep red color:

   _____

   r. a clover-type plant which is fed to cows: _____

   s. a system which lets you code a secret message: _____

WORD LIST

English	Spanish	Arabic	English	Spanish	Arabic
admiral	almirante	al-amir-al	cotton	algodón	al-qutn
alchemy	alquimia	al-kimiya	crimson	carmesí	quirmizi
alcohol	alcohol	al-kuhl	Gibraltar	Gibraltar	Djebel-Tarik
alfalfa	alfalfa	al-fasfasah	jar	jarra	jarrah
algebra	álgebra	al-jebr	orange	naranja	naranj
alkali	álcali	al-qaliy	saffron	azafrán	zafaran
apricot	albaricoque	al-birquq	sugar	azúcar	sukkar
artichoke	alcachofa	al-kharshof	zenith	cenit	samt
checkmate	jaque mate	shah mat	zero	cero	sifr
cipher	cifra	sifr			

TEST / REPASO   Unidad 10
ESTRUCTURA

Test 1   Las relaciones de Carlos   Describe the relationships between Carlos and the people in parentheses by filling in the blanks with the corresponding object pronouns.

   ⟋⟍ (el profesor de historia)   No ___*lo*___ escucha.

1. (Ana)   No _____ comprende.

2. (Teresa)   _____ manda regalos.

3. (sus primos)   No _____ escribe nunca.

4. (Felipe y Emilio)   _____ invita a su casa.

5. (su novia)   _____ llama por teléfono todos los días.

6. (yo)   No _____ dice la verdad.

7. (Paco)   _____ presta sus discos.

8. (tú)   _____ ayuda con la tarea.

9. (Ud.)   _____ pide dinero.

10. (Carmen y Pedro)   _____ invita a menudo al cine.

11. (Luisa y Margarita)   _____ escribe de vez en cuando.

12. (nosotros)   No _____ escucha nunca.

Test 2   Sí y no   Federico tells Beatriz to do certain things and not to do others. Complete his suggestions by filling in the appropriate affirmative or negative command forms of the verbs in parentheses.

(hablar)   ⟋⟍ ___*Habla*___ inglés.

         No ___*hables*___ italiano.

(comprar)   1. _____ discos.

         2. No _____ libros.

(pensar)   3. _____ en las vacaciones.

         4. No _____ en tu futuro.

(aprender)   5. _____ inglés.

         6. No _____ francés.

(volver)   7. _____ a las doce.

         8. No _____ a las dos.

(jugar)   9. _____ al tenis.

         10. No _____ al béisbol.

(escribir)   11. _____ *le* a tu prima.

         12. No le _____ a Antonio.

Test 3 Unos consejos *(Advice)*   Jaime tells Raúl to do certain things. Complete his advice by writing in the command forms of the verbs in parentheses.

1. (poner)   ¡_____ un disco de música clásica!

2. (salir)   ¡_____ con nosotros!

3. (ir)   ¡_____ al cine con tu novia!

4. (decir)   ¡_____ siempre la verdad!

5. (tener)   ¡_____ paciencia con tus hermanos!

6. (hacer)   ¡_____ algo útil!

7. (ser)   ¡_____ más generoso!

8. (venir)   ¡_____ aquí a las dos!

Test 4 De prisa *(In a hurry)*   Anita left a list of things for her brother to do and not to do. She was in such a hurry that she left out the words in parentheses. Write them in where they belong.

1. (me)   ¡_____ lláma _____ a las dos!

2. (la)   Llama a Susana por teléfono y ¡_____ invíta _____ a la fiesta!

3. (le)   ¡No _____ prestes _____ tus discos a Ramón!

4. (los)   ¡Escucha mis discos pero no _____ rompas _____!

5. (te)   ¡_____ quéda _____ en casa!

6. (te)   ¡No _____ acuestes _____ antes de las diez!

Test 5 Intérprete   Give the Spanish equivalents of the following sentences.

1. *Buy the record and lend it to me.* _____

_____

2. *Buy the magazines and send them to me.* _____

_____

3. *Buy the book, but do not send it to me.* _____

_____

4. *Buy the newspapers, but do not send them to me.* _____

_____

VOCABULARIO

Test 6 Un hijo servicial   Carlos wanted to help his mother set the table, but he forgot to bring a few things. Look at the illustration and say whether or not the following objects and foods are on the table. Check **sí** or **no**, as appropriate.

		sí	no				sí	no
☜	un plato	☒	☐	10.	el pollo		☐	☐
1.	los huevos	☐	☐	11.	el jamón		☐	☐
2.	el tenedor	☐	☐	12.	la sal		☐	☐
3.	los helados	☐	☐	13.	el azúcar		☐	☐
4.	el pastel	☐	☐	14.	la mantequilla		☐	☐
5.	las naranjas	☐	☐	15.	el pan		☐	☐
6.	los plátanos	☐	☐	16.	las peras		☐	☐
7.	el cuchillo	☐	☐	17.	las manzanas		☐	☐
8.	el queso	☐	☐	18.	el maíz		☐	☐
9.	la taza	☐	☐					

Test 7 **La carrera** *(The race)*   A few friends decided to have a race. Give the positions of the following people by completing the sentences below with the word in parentheses which is most appropriate.

Felipe   Alberto   Raúl   Susana   Isabel

1. Isabel está _____ del perro.   (detrás / delante)

2. Felipe está _____ de la casa.   (cerca / lejos)

3. Alberto está a la _____ de Raúl.   (izquierda / derecha)

4. Los chicos van _____ la casa.   (sobre / hacia)

5. Susana está _____ de Raúl.   (al lado / alrededor)

6. Alberto, Raúl y Susana están _____ de Felipe.   (debajo / delante)

CULTURA

Test 8 **¿Sí o no?**   Indicate whether the information in the following statements is accurate or not by circling **sí** or **no**.

sí   no   1. Although not originally native to the area, bananas constitute one of the basic foods of Caribbean cooking.

sí   no   2. Bananas are prepared in a variety of ways, and are often cooked.

sí   no   3. In Hispanic countries, breakfast is usually a light meal.

sí   no   4. Lunch is a complete, hot meal which includes soup, meat, vegetables and dessert.

sí   no   5. Dinner is served around six o'clock.

sí   no   6. In Hispanic countries, dinner is lighter than lunch.

sí   no   7. When Isabel García marries Pedro Ruiz, she will go by the name Isabel García de Ruiz.

sí   no   8. In Hispanic countries, people earn less money than in the United States because they work much less.

sí   no   9. Hispanic teenagers do not have record players because they do not like music.

sí   no   10. Hispanic teenagers spend less money than their American counterparts.

ACTIVITY Answers

UNIDAD 1

LECCIÓN 1

1. Me llamo; Eres; soy; te llamas; Me llamo, tú; Me llamo

2.

Andrew	Caroline
Anthony	Claire
Charles	Christine
Frederick	Helen
Philip	Emily
Francis	Frances
James	Jane
Joseph	Julie
John	Lucy
Louis	Louise
Michael	Mary
Peter	Rachel
Raymond	Rose
Richard	Susan
Thomas	Theresa

Andrés, José, Ramón, Tomás

6

Lucía, María

15

3. (Answers will vary.)

Geografía

1. Fresno, Palo Alto, Sacramento, San Diego, San Francisco, San Jose, Santa Ana, Santa Barbara
2. Pueblo
3. Pensacola
4. Las Vegas
5. Albuquerque, Santa Fe
6. Amarillo, El Paso, Laredo, San Antonio

LECCIÓN 2

1.
1. Qué; Muy
2. Hola, Cómo; Muy bien, Y tú
3. Buenos; Buenos días, Cómo, usted

2.
1. Buenos días, Sr. Castro. ¿Cómo está Ud.?
2. Buenos días, Srta. Pérez. ¿Cómo está Ud.?
3. Hola, Carlos. ¿Cómo estás?
4. Hola, Carmen. ¿Cómo estás?
5. Buenos días, Sra. de Ochoa. ¿Cómo está Ud.?
6. Hola, Manuel. ¿Cómo estás?

3.
1. ¡Buenos días!
2. ¡Buenas noches!
3. ¡Buenas tardes!
4. ¡Buenas noches!
5. ¡Buenos días!
6. ¡Buenos días!

LECCIÓN 3

AV1. (Answers will vary.)

AV2.
1. cuarenta pesetas;
   quince pesetas;
   cincuenta y cinco pesetas
2. veinte y dos pesetas;
   cuarenta y cinco pesetas;
   sesenta y siete pesetas
3. treinta pesetas;
   sesenta y seis pesetas;
   noventa y seis pesetas
4. cuarenta pesetas;
   treinta pesetas;
   setenta pesetas

BV1. Cuánto; . . . cinco; ¡Setenta y cinco!; ¡Sesenta!; ¡Setenta!; ¡Sesenta y cinco!

LECCIÓN 4

BV1.
1. Es la una y cinco.
   No, es la una.
2. Son las diez y cinco.
   No, son las diez.
3. Son las tres y veinte.
   No, son las tres y cuarto.
4. Son las cinco menos veinte y cinco.
   No, son las cuatro y media.

BV2.
1. . . . a las siete y veinte y cinco de la mañana.
2. Llega a Madrid a las dos menos veinte y cinco de la tarde.
3. Llega a Toledo a las tres y diez de la tarde.
4. Llega a Córdoba a las ocho menos cinco de la noche.
5. Llega a Sevilla a las diez y cinco de la noche.

¿Eres buen intérprete?

station, hotel, restaurant, bank, theater, cinema, hospital, pharmacy

LECCIÓN 5

V1.
1. siete . . .
2. seis de mayo
3. cinco de mayo
4. dos de mayo
5. cuatro de mayo

V2. (Answers will vary.)

V3.
1. el 21 de abril	el 21 de mayo
2. el 22 de mayo	el 21 de junio
3. el 22 de junio	el 22 de julio
4. el 23 de julio	el 23 de agosto
5. el 24 de agosto	el 23 de septiembre
6. el 24 de septiembre	el 23 de octubre
7. el 24 de octubre	el 22 de noviembre
8. el 23 de noviembre	el 21 de diciembre
9. el 22 de diciembre	el 20 de enero
10. el 21 de enero	el 18 de febrero
11. el 19 de febrero	el 20 de marzo

Medios de transporte

a) taxi

b) autobús, helicóptero, bicicleta, moto, tren

c) avión, coche

LECCIÓN 6

BV1. (Answers will vary.)

BV2. (Answers will vary.)

¿Eres buen intérprete?

dentist, mechanic, electrician, actor, photographer, programmer, interpreter, model, pianist, artist

EL RINCÓN CULTURAL

Direcciones

Colombia: Trinidad
Ecuador: Claudia
Perú: Héctor
Bolivia: Graciela
Chile: Esteban
Argentina: Guillermo
Uruguay: Joaquín
Paraguay: Fabiola

La tarjeta turística

(Answers will vary.)

Happy New Year

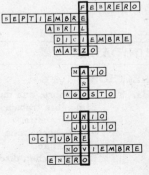

VOCABULARY

1.	a.	vent	**2.**	a.	solar	**3.**	a.	calorimeter	**4.**	a.	frigid
	b.	ventilator		b.	solstice		b.	calorie		b.	refrigerate
	c.	ventilate		c.	solarium		c.	caloric		c.	refrigerator

UNIDAD 2

LECCIÓN 1

B1.
1. Estudio inglés. Canto y toco el piano.
2. Me llamo Antonio Ramos. Hablo español, francés e inglés. Estudio arquitectura. Toco la guitarra y escucho música.
3. Me llamo Juan Carlos Suárez. Hablo español e inglés. Trabajo en un laboratorio. Escucho música popular y canto.

C1.
1. Yo (también, no) hablo francés.
2. Yo (también, no) estudio italiano.
3. Yo (también, no) trabajo mucho.
4. Yo (también, no) trabajo en Puerto Rico.
5. Yo (también, no) toco la guitarra.
6. Yo (también, no) canto muy bien.

C2.
1. Canto siempre.
   No canto bien.
2. Estudio francés.
   No estudio electrónica.
3. Escucho música clásica.
   No escucho música «disco».

Yo
(Answers will vary.)

LECCIÓN 2

A1.
1. viaja. Gana mucho dinero. Escucha la radio.
2. bailan y escuchan música. No trabajan.
3. trabajan mucho y ganan mucho dinero. No estudian.

B1.
1. Estudio; Estudia mucho ella; No estudia mucho.
2. Bailo; Bailan bien ellos; Ellos; No bailan bien.
3. Canto; Cantan bien ellos; Ellos; No cantan bien.

B2. (Answers will vary.)

Mi familia
(Answers will vary.)

LECCIÓN 3

A1.
1. ¿Nadas?
2. ¿Trabaja Ud.?
3. ¿Viajas?
4. ¿Trabajas?

B1.
1. espera
2. espera
3. esperas
4. espero
5. espera
6. esperan
7. esperan
8. espera

C1.
1. ¿Quiénes trabajan?
   ¿Dónde trabajan?
   Trabajan
2. ¿Quién toca la guitarra?
   ¿Dónde toca la guitarra?
   Toca
3. ¿Quiénes nadan?
   ¿Dónde nadan?
   Nadan

C2.
1. Dónde estudias
2. Por qué estudias fotografía
3. Con quién viajas
4. Dónde trabajas
5. Cuándo viajas

Una carta
(Answers will vary.)

LECCIÓN 4

B1.
1. Estudio; Estudian; estudio, estudia
2. trabajan; trabajo; trabajas; Trabajo; trabajan; trabajamos
3. habla; Hablo; habla; habla; Hablan; hablamos
4. nadan; nadan; Nadas; nadar, Nado

C1. (Answers will vary.)

D1.
1. Tú trabajas para ella.
   Ella trabaja para ti.
2. Él trabaja con ellos.
   Ellos trabajan con él.
3. Ellas trabajan para él.
   Él trabaja para ellas.
4. Yo trabajo con ella.
   Ella trabaja conmigo.
5. Tú trabajas con él.
   Él trabaja contigo.

EL RINCÓN CULTURAL

La geografía norteamericana

Anuncios y actividades

1. bailar 2. mirar la televisión 3. estudiar 4. escuchar música 5. viajar 6. ganar dinero 7. tocar la guitarra

VOCABULARY

1.	a.	ball	**4.**	a.	Esperanto
	b.	ballroom		b.	despair
	c.	ballet		c.	desperate
	d.	ballerina		d.	desperation
2.	a.	cantatas	**5.**	a.	necessity
	b.	cantor		b.	unnecessary
	c.	chant		c.	necessitous
3.	a.	mirror		d.	necessitate
	b.	mirage			

UNIDAD 3

LECCIÓN 1

B1.
1. un hombre, una mujer
   El hombre trabaja.
   La mujer mira.
2. un muchacho, una muchacha
   Ellos bailan.
   Ellos escuchan discos.
3. un chico, una chica, una mujer
   El chico toca la guitarra.
   La chica canta.
   La mujer escucha.

C1. 1. es; estudia
 2. son; estudian
 3. eres; trabajas
 4. somos; trabajamos
 5. es; viaja
 6. soy; viajo
 7. es; trabaja
 8. son; estudian

¿Eres buen(a) detective?
1. Hay una estudiante. La estudiante es Silvia.
2. Hay un detective. El detective es Roberto.
3. Hay una actriz. La actriz es Inés.
4. Hay una artista. La artista es Carmen.
5. Hay un actor. El actor es José.
6. Hay un fotógrafo. El fotógrafo es Luis.
7. Hay una doctora. La doctora es María.
8. Hay un estudiante. El estudiante es Antonio.

LECCIÓN 2

B1. bajo, alto (Order and endings will vary.)
 guapo, feo
 delgado, gordo
 rubio, moreno
 tonto, inteligente
 divertido, serio
 antipático, simpático
 interesante, aburrido
 bueno, malo

B2. (Answers will vary.)

Críticas
 (Answers will vary.)

LECCIÓN 3

B1. 1. somos; Tenemos libros.
 2. soy; Tengo una raqueta.
 3. es; Tiene un clarinete.
 4. eres; Tienes una guitarra.
 5. es; Tiene un estetoscopio.
 6. son; Tienen cámaras.

B2. a) discos, tres libros, una revista y una cinta.
 b) tres relojes, dos grabadoras, un tocadiscos, cinco cintas y tres bolígrafos.

C1. 1. . . . un tocadiscos (viejo).
 2. Hay unos discos. Los discos son (nuevos).
 3. Hay un radio. El radio es (barato).
 4. Hay una grabadora. La grabadora es (cara).
 5. También hay un televisor. El televisor es (grande).
 6. Hay un coche. El coche es (pequeño).
 7. Hay una bicicleta. La bicicleta es (bonita).
 8. Hay una moto. La moto es (nueva).

Tus posesiones
 (Answers will vary.)

LECCIÓN 4

B1. (Answers will vary.)
V1. 1. es un atleta mexicano. Tiene diez y nueve años.
 2. es un atleta español. Tiene diez y ocho años.
 3. es una atleta norteamericana. Tiene diez y seis años.
 4. es una atleta puertorriqueña. Tiene diez y siete años.
 5. es un atleta cubano. Tiene veinte y dos años.
 6. es una atleta española. Tiene veinte años.

C1. 1. . . . los chicos que nadan?
 2. ¿Quiénes son los chicos que bailan?
 3. ¿Quién es la chica que escucha discos?
 4. ¿Quién es la chica que toca el piano?

¡Un poco de lógica, por favor!
 (Answers will vary.)

EL RINCÓN CULTURAL

El zodíaco
 (Answers will vary.)
¿Cómo son?
 (Answers will vary.)

VOCABULARY

1. a. amicable, amiable
   b. unamiable
   c. amity
2. a. human
   b. humanity
   c. humane
   d. humanitarian
   e. dehumanize
3. a. juvenile
   b. junior
   c. rejuvenate
4. a. headmaster
   b. master
   c. mastery
   d. magistrate
5. a. library
   b. librarian
6. a. alto
   b. altitude
   c. altimeter
7. a. bass
   b. basement
   c. debase
   d. basset
   e. base
8. a. malady
   b. malignant
   c. malice
   d. malfunctioning
9. a. novice
   b. novelty
   c. renovate
10. a. tenure
    b. tenacious
    c. obtain
    d. maintain

UNIDAD 4

LECCIÓN 1

A1. 1. a Antonio. No mira el libro.
 2. a Isabel. No espera a Lucía.
 3. el disco. No escucha a Bárbara.
 4. revistas. No compra discos.
 5. el autobús. No espera a los chicos.

V1. 1. compran   5. habla
 2. compramos   6. lleva
 3. enseña   7. saca
 4. llegas

B1. 1. Roberto invita a la chica norteamericana al club.
 2. Los chicos invitan a las chicas al concierto.
 3. Carmen invita al chico mexicano al café.
 4. La profesora invita al fotógrafo al cine.
 5. Las chicas invitan a los chicos a la discoteca.

B2. 1. habla de la chica
 2. hablan de los muchachos
 3. habla del alumno
 4. hablan de las alumnas
 5. habla del profesor
 6. habla del hombre
 7. hablan de las estudiantes
 8. habla del estudiante
 9. habla de la maestra
 10. habla de la mujer

LECCIÓN 2

A1.
1. son; Están en el teatro.
2. eres; Estás en el aeropuerto.
3. soy; Estoy en el hospital.
4. son; Están en el museo.
5. somos; Estamos en la escuela.
6. es; Está en la farmacia.
7. es; Está en el laboratorio.

C1. (Answers will vary.)

Una entrevista
1. Eres mexicano(a)
2. De dónde eres
3. Dónde está
4. Está cerca de
5. Estudias mucho en casa
6. Vas, a la casa
7. Adónde vas
8. Vas a Nueva York
9. Vas a visitar Washington
10. Adónde vas

LECCIÓN 3

A1. (Answers will vary.)

A2.
1. ¿Dónde está el Hotel Continental?
   Está en la calle de Colón.
   Es un hotel . . .
   ¡No, es un hotel muy moderno!
2. ¿Dónde está el Café Inglés?
   Está en la calle de Segovia.
   Es un café . . .
   ¡No, es un café muy pequeño!
3. ¿Dónde está el museo azteca?
   Está en la Plaza Santo Domingo.
   Es un museo . . .
   ¡No, es un museo muy grande!
4. ¿Dónde está el restaurante Flamenco?
   Está en la calle Goya.
   Es un restaurante . . .
   ¡No, es un restaurante muy barato!

B1. (Answers will vary.)

¿Quién soy yo?
1. (John)
2. Soy de (los Estados Unidos).
3. Tengo (catorce) años.
4. Soy (alto) y (moreno).
5. Soy (un alumno) (bueno).
6. Ahora estoy (en casa).
7. Estoy (cansado).

LECCIÓN 4

A1.
1. (No) lo invito a la fiesta. (No) lo llevo . . .
2. (No) la invito a la fiesta. (No) la llevo . . .
3. (No) los invito a la fiesta. (No) los llevo . . .
4. (No) las invito a la fiesta. (No) las llevo . . .
5. (No) los invito a la fiesta. (No) los llevo . . .

A2.
1. no lo necesitan. lo necesita.
2. los necesitamos. no los necesitas.
3. no la necesita. la necesitan.
4. lo necesitas. lo necesito.
5. no la necesita. la necesita.
6. no las necesita. las necesita.
7. no lo necesitas. lo necesita.
8. lo necesitan. lo necesita.

A3.
1. Los escuchan Inés y Esteban.
2. Las llevan Elena y Luisa.
3. Lo tienen Inés y Esteban.
4. Las compra Carmen.
5. Lo esperan Elena y Luisa.

B1.
1. Hoy no. Pero voy a buscarlas mañana.
2. Hoy no. Pero voy a invitarlos mañana.
3. Hoy no. Pero voy a esucharla mañana.
4. Hoy no. Pero voy a estudiarla mañana.

EL RINCÓN CULTURAL

En el avión
   (Answers will vary.)

La casa de cambio	En el hotel
1. 70	8. Alfonso X
2. 1,401	10. ALFONSOTEL
3. 700, 7,000	11. 21 44 00
En el tren	12. 780; $11; No
4. July 29	13. 168; $2.40; Yes
5. 8:27	
6. 667; $9.50	
7. first	

VOCABULARY

1. a. campus
   b. camp
   c. encampment
2. a. marina
   b. Maritime
   c. submarine
   d. mariner
   e. marine
3. a. Pisces
   b. piscatorial
4. a. population
   b. popular
   c. depopulate
   d. pueblo
5. a. barge
   b. embark
   c. disembark
   d. Embarcadero
6. a. infirmary
   b. infirmities
   c. firm
7. a. aviary
   b. aviator
   c. aviation
   d. avian

UNIDAD 5

LECCIÓN 1

A1.
1. trabaja, vive
2. trabajo, vivo
3. trabajan, viven
4. trabajan, viven
5. (Answers will vary.)

A2.
1. leo; escribe
2. leemos; escriben
3. lee; escribo
4. lees; escribe
5. leen; escriben

B1.
1. vivo, aprendo
2. Bebe, come
3. trabaja; Vende
4. Comprenden, habla
5. Ve; creo
6. leemos, comprendemos
7. comprendo; aprendes
8. viven; Asisten

C1.
1. Es el radio de Rafael.
2. Es el coche de María.
3. Son los libros de Rafael.
4. Es el reloj del Sr. López.
5. Es el lápiz de Rafael.
6. Es el televisor de María.

LECCIÓN 2

A1. (Answers will vary.)

A2.
1. tu; Mi grabadora; La tiene
2. tus; Mis cintas; Las tiene
3. tu; Mi reloj; Lo tiene
4. tus; Mis libros; Los tiene

B1. 1. Mi profesor(a) de inglés es . . .
2. Mi profesor(a) de matemáticas es . . .
3. Mi profesor(a) de ciencias es . . .
4. Mi profesor(a) de historia es . . .
5. Mi profesor(a) de educación física es. . .

C1. 1. estás; Haces
2. está; Hace
3. estamos; Hacemos
4. está; Hace
5. estoy; Hago

Mi familia
(Answers will vary.)

LECCIÓN 3

V1. 1. La segunda es el número doce.
2. La tercera es el número cinco.
3. El cuarto es el número cuatro.
4. La quinta es el número treinta.
5. El sexto es el número diez.
6. El séptimo es el número veinte.
7. La octava es el número ocho.
8. El noveno es el número tres.
9. El décimo es el número nueve.

A1. 1. dice; También hace cosas interesantes.
2. digo; También hago cosas inteligentes.
3. dicen; También hacen cosas cómicas.
4. dice; También hace cosas divertidas.
5. decimos; También hacemos cosas extraordinarias.
6. dices; También haces tonterías.

B1. 1. . . . guitarra y su bolso.
2. va a buscar su bicicleta, su guitarra y sus discos.
3. . . . va a buscar su radio y su reloj.
4. . . . van a buscar sus gatos y su perro.

B2. 1. tus; Cómo están sus hermanos
2. tu; Va a invitar a su primo a la fiesta
3. tus; Ve a sus amigos franceses a menudo
4. tus; Tiene sus discos con Ud.

Tu casa
1. Nuestra; es . . .
2. Nuestro; es . . .
3. Nuestra; es . . .
4. Nuestros; son . . .
5. Nuestro; es . . .

LECCIÓN 4

A1. 1. su
2. su, sus
3. nuestros, nuestros
4. mi, mis, mis, mi
5. su, sus

C1. 1. da . . . consejos
2. dan . . . consejos
3. da . . . consejos
4. doy . . . consejos
5. damos . . . consejos

D1. 1. les doy . . .
2. le doy . . .
3. le doy . . .
4. le doy . . .
5. le doy . . .
6. les doy . . .

D2. 1. Le; No le escribe.
2. Las; No los llama por teléfono.
3. Lo; No las ayuda.
4. Le; No les da buenos consejos.
5. Les; No le dice cosas divertidas.
6. Le; No le manda cartas.

¿Te importa la gente?
(Answers will vary.)

EL RINCÓN CULTURAL

Un anuncio de nacimiento
1. la clínica la merced
2. subtract 1959 from current year
3. Alfredo Peña Ogliastri
4. Ogliastri

Una esquela matrimonial
1. San Juan
2. Santa Iglesia Catedral
3. December 31
4. 11:00 a.m.
5. Hotel El Convento

Ramón O. Almodóvar Torres
Almodóvar
Torres
María del Carmen Díaz de Almodóvar
Díaz

Efrer Morales Serrano
Morales
Serrano
Anita Amaral de Morales
Amaral

VOCABULARY

1. a. bib
   b. imbibe
   c. beverage
2. a. comestible
   b. comestibles
3. a. incredible
   b. credulous
   c. credibility
   d. credentials
4. a. dictate
   b. dictator
   c. diction
   d. predict
5. a. scribbling
   b. scribe
   c. script
6. a. legible
   b. lecture
   c. illegible
7. a. vendor
   b. vending
8. a. invisible
   b. visibility
   c. videotape
9. a. maternal
   b. maternity
10. a. paternal
    b. paternalism
11. a. primer
    b. primaries
    c. primary
    d. prime
12. a. octave
    b. octagon
    c. October

UNIDAD 6

LECCIÓN 1

A1. 1. Sí, (No, no) te invito al cine.
2. Sí, (No, no) te enseño mis fotos.
3. Sí, (No, no) te ayudo con la tarea.
4. Sí, (No, no) te hablo de mis planes.
5. Sí, (No, no) voy a invitarte a mi fiesta de cumpleaños.
6. Sí, (No, no) voy a prestarte diez dólares.

B1. 1. No come nada.
2. No bebe nada.
3. No llama a nadie.
4. No invita a nadie a la casa.
5. No hace nada.
6. No habla con nadie.

B2. 1. no hace nunca las tareas
2. no van nunca a la escuela
3. no comes nunca en la cafetería
4. no escuchan nunca las cintas
5. no hablamos nunca con el profesor
6. no aprendo nunca cosas tontas

C1. 1. pide (cien) dólares
2. piden (doce) dólares
3. pido (seis) dólares
4. pides (treinta y cinco) dólares
5. pide (un) dólar
6. pide (diez) dólares
7. piden (catorce) dólares
8. pedimos (ochenta y cinco) dólares

El presupuesto de la semana
(Answers will vary.)

LECCIÓN 2

A1.
1. jugamos
2. juegas
3. juega
4. juegan
5. juego

B1. (Answers will vary.)
B2. (Answers will vary.)
C1.
1. Me gusta el cine ... pero no me gusta la violencia.
2. Me gusta la televisión ... pero no me gustan los programas aburridos.
3. Me gustan los deportes ... pero no me gustan los deportes violentos.
4. Me gustan las ciudades grandes ... pero no me gusta la contaminación del aire.

C2. (Answers will vary.)
Entre amigos
1. ¿Te gustan los deportes?
2. ¿Tiene tu escuela un equipo de fútbol?
3. ¿Hay jugadores buenos en España?
4. ¿Juegas al tenis?
5. ¿Juegan los españoles al fútbol norteamericano?

LECCIÓN 3

B1.
1. (No) pierdo el tiempo.
2. (No) pierde el tiempo.
3. (No) pierde el tiempo.
4. (No) pierden el tiempo.
5. (No) perdemos el tiempo.
6. (No) pierdes el tiempo.
7. (No) pierden el tiempo.
8. (No) perdemos el tiempo.

C1.
1. Paco tiene una cita con Inés. La encuentra en su oficina.
2. Elena y Carmen tienen una cita con sus novios. Los encuentran en el restaurante.
3. Tenemos una cita con unas amigas. Las encontramos en las tiendas.
4. Tengo una cita con Ramón. Lo encuentro en el cine.
5. Tienes una cita con Isabel. La encuentras en el centro.
6. Uds. tienen una cita con unos amigos. Los encuentran en la playa.

C2. (Answers will vary.)
Entre amigos
1. Sí, (No, no) quiero ir al cine.
2. Prefiero las películas del oeste (románticas).
3. La película cuesta (tres) dólares.
4. La película empieza a las (siete).
5. Sí, (No, no) te entiendo cuando hablas español.
6. Sí, (No, no) recuerdo quien es el actor.
7. Sí, (No, no) puedo prestarte un dólar.
8. Sí, (No, no) puedo prestarte cien dólares.
9. Sí, (No, no) puedo encontrarte mañana.
10. Sí, (No, no) puedo ayudarte.

LECCIÓN 4

A1.
1. El jueves es el día
2. El lunes es el día
3. El viernes es el día
4. El martes es el día

A2. (Answers will vary.)
B1.
1. salen con ...
2. salgo con ...
3. sales con ...
4. salimos con ...
5. sale con ...

B2.
1. Los pone en la maleta.
2. La pongo en la maleta.
3. No la pones en la maleta.
4. No lo ponen en la maleta.
5. Lo ponemos en la maleta.
6. No lo pone en la maleta.

C1.
1. lo reconocen ... pero no lo conocen personalmente.
2. la reconoce ... pero no la conoce personalmente.
3. lo reconoces ... pero no lo conoces personalmente.
4. los reconozco ... pero no los conozco personalmente.
5. la reconocemos ... pero no la conocemos personalmente.

Entre amigos
1. Sí, (No, no) salgo a menudo.
2. Salgo con (mis amigos).
3. Salgo los (viernes).
4. Sí, (No, no) tengo un coche.
5. Sí, (No, no) conduzco un coche. Es el coche de (mi papá).
6. Sí, (No, no) tengo muchos discos.
7. Sí, (No, no) los llevo a las fiestas.
8. Sí, (No, no) conozco a unos (ningunos) chicos hispanos.
9. Sí, (No, no) conozco a unas (ningunas) chicas hispanas.

EL RINCÓN CULTURAL

¡Béisbol!

b) New York	o) Philadelphia
c) Cleveland	p) Pittsburgh
d) Toronto	q) St. Louis
e) Boston	r) Montreal
f) Baltimore	s) New York
g) Milwaukee	t) Chicago
h) California	u) San Francisco
i) Kansas City	v) Atlanta
j) Minnesota	w) San Diego
k) Oakland	x) Los Angeles
l) Texas	y) Houston
m) Chicago	z) Cincinnati
n) Seattle	

Para entender el béisbol en español

pitcher	home run
hit	walk
single	stolen base
double	run
triple	inning

VOCABULARY

1. a. dormitory
   b. dormant
2. a. reconnaissance
   b. connoisseur
   c. recognize
   d. incognito
3. a. waste
   b. devastate
4. a. juggle
   b. joke
   c. jocular
   d. joker
5. a. petition
   b. petitioner
6. a. deposit
   b. depose
   c. impose
   d. position
7. a. record
   b. records
8. a. revolver
   b. revolve
   c. revolution
   d. evolution

UNIDAD 7

LECCIÓN 1

A1. (Answers will vary.)
B1.
1. Carmen es menos delgada que Luisa, pero es más delgada que Marisela.
2. Carmen es menos fuerte que Marisela, pero es más fuerte que Luisa.
3. Marisela es menos atlética que Carmen, pero es más atlética que Luisa.

B2. (Answers will vary.)
C1.
1. El restaurante más barato es . . .
2. El mejor restaurante es . . .
3. El hotel más moderno es . . .
4. El hotel más grande es . . .
5. La escuela más moderna es . . .
6. La mejor escuela es . . .
7. Las tiendas más elegantes son . . .
8. Las tiendas más baratas son . . .

Las comparaciones
(Answers will vary.)

LECCIÓN 2

V1.
1. . . . amarilla
2. verde, blanca, roja y castaña
3. azul, blanca y amarilla
4. amarilla, azul, roja y blanca
5. amarilla, azul, roja, blanca y negra

A1.
1. aquel
2. aquellos
3. aquella
4. aquellos, aquel

B1. (Answers will vary.)
V2.
1. ¿Cuánto cuesta esta . . .
   . . . cuesta trescientas pesetas.
   Cuesta solamente noventa.
2. ¿Cuánto cuestan estos zapatos?
   Por lo general, cuestan quinientas pesetas.
   ¿Y ahora?
   Cuestan solamente trescientas.
3. ¿Cuánto cuestan estas sandalias?
   Por lo general, cuestan cuatrocientas pesetas.
   ¿Y ahora?
   Cuestan solamente doscientas.

¿Cuál ropa?
(Answers will vary.)

LECCIÓN 3

A1.
1. Yo me preparo.
2. Carlos no se prepara.
3. Tú no te preparas.
4. Nosotros nos preparamos.
5. Felipe y Francisco no se preparan.
6. Ud. se prepara.
7. Uds. no se preparan.

A2. (Answers will vary.)
B1.
1. se
2. nos
3. te
4. me
5. se
6. se

B2.
1. se baña
2. se visten
3. se lava las manos y se lava la cara

¿Cómo te vistes?
(Answers will vary.)

LECCIÓN 4

A1.
1. las manos
2. los brazos, las piernas
3. las manos
4. los pies, la cabeza, las manos

5. la mano, la mano derecha;
   el brazo derecho (la mano derecha), el brazo izquierdo (la mano izquierda)
6. los pies

B1.
1. Se despierta a las (cuatro) de la tarde. Se acuesta a las (ocho) de la mañana.
2. Nos despertamos a las (tres) de la mañana. Nos acostamos a las (siete) de la noche.
3. Se despiertan a las (diez) de la mañana. Se acuestan a las (dos) de la mañana.
4. Te despiertas a las (siete) de la mañana. Te acuestas a las (once) de la noche.

B2.
1. Me lavo. Después me visto.
2. Te despiertas. Después te levantas.
3. se baña. Después se peina.
4. se lava. Después se pone perfume.

B3. (Answers will vary.)
B4. (Answers will vary.)

Tus hábitos
1. Sí, (No, no) me divierto en la escuela.
2. Sí, (No, no) me divierto con mis amigos.
3. Me acuesto los sábados a las (doce).
4. Me levanto los domingos a las (diez).
5. Sí, (No, no) me quedo en casa los domingos.

EL RINCÓN CULTURAL

El arte de la publicidad
1. sweaters, sweatshirts, skirts, pants, blouses
2. $2.00
3. $8.99
4. Mexico
5. white, blue, yellow and beige
6. pants and shoes
7. dresses
8. flores naturales
9. florería
10. Jocarri
11. gardenias, carnations, camellias, african violets, gladioli, bird-of-paradise, roses, iris, orchids, chrysanthemums
12. toothbrush
13. un cepillo
14. Tek
15. 3

VOCABULARY

1. a. restrictive
   b. strict
   c. constrictor
2. a. curt
   b. curtail
3. a. fortress, fortification
   b. fortify
   c. comfort
4. a. debilitating
   b. debility
   c. debilitate
5. a. amelioration
   b. ameliorate
6. a. oculist
   b. binoculars
   c. monocle
   d. ocular
7. a. corporal
   b. corpse
   c. corpulent
   d. corpuscle
   e. corps
8. a. pelt
   b. depilatory
9. a. pedestrian
   b. centipede
   c. pedicure
   d. pedal
10. a. manuscript
    b. manicure
    c. manage
    d. manual
    e. manacles
11. a. vestments
    b. divest
    c. vestry

UNIDAD 8

LECCIÓN 1

A1.
1. acabamos de; No vamos a celebrar.
2. acaba de; Va a celebrar.
3. acaban de; Van a celebrar.
4. acabas de; No vas a celebrar.
5. acaban de; Van a celebrar.

A2. (Answers will vary.)

B1.
1. Hace veinte años que vive Manuel aquí.
2. Hace quince años que vive el Sr. Abastado aquí.
3. Hace dos años que vivimos aquí.
4. Hace cuatro semanas que vives aquí.
5. Hace tres meses que viven Felipe y Susana aquí.

B2.
1. sales; Hace un año que salgo . . .
2. trabajas; Hace unas semanas que trabajo . . .
3. estudias; Hace seis meses que estudio . . .
4. tienes; Hace dos semanas que tengo . . .

B3.
1. Sí, hace unos ciento sesenta años que México es un país independiente.
2. Sí, hace unos setenta años que el Nuevo México es un estado.
3. Sí, hace unos sesenta años que los puertorriqueños son ciudadanos norteamericanos.

¿Por cuánto tiempo?
1. Hace . . . que vivo en esta ciudad.
2. Hace . . . que asisto a esta escuela.
3. Hace . . . que estudio español.

LECCIÓN 2

A1.
1. compró; Gastó mil ciento sesenta pesetas.
2. compraron; Gastaron mil quinientas pesetas.
3. compraron; Gastaron ochocientas pesetas.
4. compré; Gasté setecientas pesetas.
5. compraste; Gastaste doscientas pesetas.
6. compramos; Gastamos mil pesetas.
7. compraron; Gastaron seiscientas pesetas.

A2.
1. habló con el presidente de los Estados Unidos
2. visitaron Disney World
3. escuchamos la Boston Pops
4. admiraron la Estatua de la Libertad
5. trabajaste en un rancho
6. visitó el barrio chino
7. escuchó jazz en el barrio francés
8. sacaron fotos de «El Álamo»

B1.
. . . pasé por él.	Sí, lo encontré.
Dejaste . . .	Tocaste . . .
. . . lo dejé allí.	Sí, la toqué . . . dos horas.
Pagaste . . .	Empezaste . . .
Sí, lo pagué.	Sí, la empecé.
Encontraste . . .	Llamaste . . .
Sí, lo encontré.	Sí, la llamé por teléfono.
Pasaste . . .	Jugaste . . .
Sí, pasé por ella.	Sí, lo jugué . . . ella.
Encontraste . . .	

Los incidentes
(Answers will vary.)

LECCIÓN 3

A1.
1. Rebeca salió con Manuel.
2. Javier y Salvador salieron con Rosa y Anita.
3. Nosotras salimos con unos chicos mexicanos.
4. Tú saliste con Andrea.
5. Yo salí con Carmen.

A2.
1. compraron una guitarra por treinta dólares. La vendieron por sesenta. Ganaron treinta dólares.
2. compré un sombrero andaluz por treinta y cinco dólares. Lo vendí por quince. Perdí veinte dólares.
3. compramos unos discos flamencos por diez dólares. Los vendimos por quince. Ganamos cinco dólares.
4. compró un bolso por veinte y cinco dólares. Lo vendió por cinco. Perdió veinte dólares.

C1.
1. rompió
2. escribió
3. leyó
4. descubrió
5. dio

C2.
1. no viste nada. Oíste algo.
2. vimos algo. Oímos algo.
3. no vio nada. No oyó nada.
4. vi algo. No oí nada.
5. no vieron nada. Oyeron algo.

C3. Miré y vi un coche con tres hombres enmascarados. El conductor se quedó en el coche mientras los otros entraron en el banco. Cinco minutos después, salieron del banco con un saco muy grande. El conductor los ayudó a poner el saco en el coche. Salieron muy de prisa.

Una página de un diario
(Answers will vary.)

LECCIÓN 4

A1.
1. Visité; Saqué
2. Encontré; Nadé; Comí
3. Vi; Salí; Escuché
4. Compré; Asistí; Aprendí

A2. (Answers will vary.)

A3.
1. jugaron ayer
2. la encontró ayer
3. la llamamos por teléfono ayer
4. le escribí ayer
5. los aprendiste ayer

B1.
1. se sintieron; Durmieron . . .
2. se sintió; Durmió . . .
3. nos sentimos; Dormimos . . .
4. te sentiste; Dormiste . . .
5. me sentí; Dormí . . .

V1.
1. tenemos hambre
2. tiene calor
3. tiene frío
4. tengo sed

El diario
(Answers will vary.)

EL RINCÓN CULTURAL

Restaurantes
un sándwich de queso, un sándwich de pollo, una tortilla de jamón, tres hamburguesas, dos perros calientes, dos cafés con leche, dos tajadas de piña

(Answers will vary.)

VOCABULARY

1. a. aquatic
   b. aquarium
   c. aqueduct
   d. aquaplane
2. a. final
   b. finale
   c. finalists
   d. finalize
3. a. vinegar
   b. vine
   c. vintage
   d. vintner
4. a. facilitate
   b. facility
   c. facile
5. a. felicity
   b. felicitous
   c. felicitate
6. a. debtor
   b. debt
   c. indebted
7. a. equivocal
   b. unequivocal
   c. equivocate
8. a. ruptured
   b. interrupt
   c. disrupt
   d. eruption

UNIDAD 9

LECCIÓN 1

A1. (Answers will vary.)

A2.
1. ¿Sabes bailar?
2. ¿Sabes sacar fotos?
3. ¿Saben Uds. dibujar?
4. ¿Saben Uds. tocar el piano?
5. ¿Saben Uds. actuar?
6. ¿Sabes cantar?

A3.
1. Conoce Ud.
2. Sabe Ud.
3. Sabe Ud.
4. Sabe Ud.
5. Conoce Ud.

B1.
1. No lo sabe.
2. No lo saben.
3. Lo sé.
4. No lo sabes.
5. Lo sabemos.

B2.
1. No lo sé.
2. No lo sé.
3. No lo sé.

¿Qué sabes hacer?
1. Sé (No sé) escribir a máquina.
2. Sé (No sé) dibujar.
3. Quiero (No quiero) ser doctor(a).
4. Quiero (No quiero) ser trabajador(a) social.

LECCIÓN 2

A1. (Answers will vary.)

B1. (Answers will vary.)

B2.
1. Antes de reparar su bicicleta, Isabel se pone pantalones viejos. Después de reparar su bicicleta, se lava las manos.
2. Antes de bañarnos, nos quitamos los pijamas. Después de bañarnos, nos vestimos.
3. Antes de escoger una refrigeradora, mi papá compara los precios. Después de escoger una refrigeradora, la paga.
4. Antes de jugar al tenis, mi prima compra una raqueta. Después de jugar al tenis, está muy cansada.

B3.
1. En vez de dormir, Felipe mira la televisión.
2. En vez de aprender los verbos, leemos una novela de aventuras.
3. En vez de trabajar, mis primos tocan la guitarra.
4. En vez de prepararte para el examen, escribes a tu novia.

C1. (Answers will vary.)

C2.
1. Los libros son para mí.
2. La cámara es para él.
3. La caja de chocolates es para ellos.
4. La raqueta es para ti.
5. El pasaporte es para Ud.

Entrevista
1. Sí, (No, no) sé conducir.
2. Sí, (No, no) aprendo a conducir.
3. Sí, (No, no) aprendo a tocar la guitarra.
4. Sí, (No, no) empiezo a hablar español bien.
5. Sí, (No, no) me olvido de estudiar a veces.
6. Sí, (No, no) necesito dormir mucho.

LECCIÓN 3

A1.
1. Fue a los Estados Unidos.
2. Fueron a Egipto.
3. Fuimos al Canadá.
4. Fuiste a Portugal.
5. Fueron a Alemania.

B1.
1. dijo
2. dijo
3. dijeron
4. dijimos
5. dijiste
6. dije

C1. (Answers will vary.)

C2. (Answers will vary.)

Una solicitud de empleo
(Answers will vary.)

LECCIÓN 4

A1.
1. puso
2. pusimos
3. puse
4. pusieron
5. pusiste
6. pusieron

A2.
1. no vino. Tuvo que . . .
2. no vine. Tuve que . . .
3. no vinieron. Tuvieron que . . .
4. no viniste. Tuviste que . . .

A3.
1. fue; Fui
2. hizo; hice
3. Vino; vino
4. dijo; dije
5. puso

B1.
1. (no) digo generalmente lo que pienso
   (no) digo generalmente lo que pienso
2. (no) comprendo generalmente lo que aprendo
   (no) comprendo generalmente lo que aprendo
3. (no) encuentro generalmente lo que busco
   (no) encuentro generalmente lo que busco
4. (no) creo generalmente lo que leo
   (no) creo generalmente lo que leo
5. (no) creo generalmente lo que oigo
   (no) creo generalmente lo que oigo

El pasado
1. Sí, (No, no) hice mis tareas ayer.
2. Sí, (No, no) hice un viaje durante las vacaciones.
3. Sí, (No, no) pude mirar la televisión anoche.

EL RINCÓN CULTURAL

Ofertas de empleo
1. bilingual secretary
2. an important international company
3. Madrid
4. 8:00-5:35
5. public relations
6. a woman
7. yes
8. Chrysler
9. Spain
10. technical translators
11. English & Spanish
12. 8:30-5:30 (9 hours)
13. sales
14. both
15. cars
16. the south of Puerto Rico
17. three
18. sales supervisor
19. permanent
20. $600
21. Spanish-American Institute
22. New York
23. office skills and English
24. April 24

VOCABULARY
1. a. advocate
   b. advocate
   c. vocal
   d. vociferous
2. a. dentures
   b. dandelion
   c. dentifrice
3. a. eloquent
   b. eloquence
   c. elocution
   d. loquacious
   e. monologue
   f. ventriloquist
4. a. mode
   b. modish
   c. outmoded
   d. modernize
5. a. single
   b. sinecure
   c. singular
6. a. antedate
   b. ante
   c. antecedents
   d. antechamber
7. a. peruse
   b. permeable
   c. perambulate

UNIDAD 10

LECCIÓN 1

A1.
1. (No) los llamo. (No) les escribo a ellos.
2. (No) lo llamo. (No) le escribo a él.
3. (No) la llamo. (No) le escribo a ella.
4. (No) los llamo. (No) les escribo a ellos.
5. (No) los llamo. (No) les escribo a ellos.

B1. (Answers will vary.)

C1.
1. ¡Acuéstate, Manuel!
2. ¡Lávate, Federico!
3. ¡Quédate en el dormitorio, Paco!
4. ¡Diviértete, Miguel!

C2. (Answers will vary.)

V1.
1. Necesito un plato, un tenedor y un cuchillo.
2. Necesitamos platos y tenedores.
3. Necesitan vasos.

Tus relaciones con los otros
1. Sí, (No, no) les ayudo a menudo.
2. Sí, (No, no) les escribo a menudo.
3. Sí, (No, no) los conozco bien.

LECCIÓN 2

V1. (Answers will vary.)

A1.
1. ¡No hables tanto, Carmen!
2. ¡No comas tanto, Ramón!
3. ¡No bebas tanto, Alberto!
4. ¡No trabajes tanto, María Luisa!
5. ¡No estudies tanto, Enrique!
6. ¡No leas tanto, Elvira!
7. ¡No duermas tanto, Elba!

A2.
1. No comas carne. Come
2. No tomes gaseosas. Toma
3. No escuches música popular. Escucha
4. No compres cosas inútiles. Compra
5. No leas historietas. Lee
6. No pidas dinero. Pide

B1.
1. ¡Invítalo!   3. ¡No las invites!
2. ¡Invítalas!   4. ¡Invítala!

B2.
1. ¡Sí, tráela!   3. ¡Sí, tráelos!
2. ¡Sí, tráela!   4. ¡No lo traigas!

B3.
1. ¡Sí, quédate en cama!
2. ¡No te bañes!
3. ¡No te sientes en el sofá!
4. ¡Sí, duérmete!

La comida y tú
(Answers will vary.)

LECCIÓN 3

A1.
1. ¡Ponla! (¡No la pongas!)
2. ¡Ponlo! (¡No lo pongas!)
3. ¡Ponlo! (¡No lo pongas!)
4. ¡Ponlo! (¡No lo pongas!)
5. ¡Ponlos! (¡No los pongas!)
6. ¡Ponlos! (¡No los pongas!)

B1.
1. Di   5. Sé
   No digas   No seas
2. Haz   6. Ve
   No hagas   No vayas
3. Da   7. Pon
   No . . . des   No pongas
4. Está   8. Sal
   No estés   No salgas

C1. (Answers will vary.)

C2.
1. Me das
   No, no te la doy.
   ¿Por qué no quieres dármela?
   Porque la
2. me compras
   No, no te la compro.
   ¿Por qué no quieres comprármela?
   Porque la
3. Me enseñas
   No, no te las enseño.
   ¿Por qué no quieres enseñármelas?
   Porque las

LECCIÓN 4

A1.
1. Ya no los tengo.
   Se los presté
2. Ya no las tengo.
   Se las mandé
3. Ya no la tengo.
   Se la di
4. Ya no las tengo.
   Se las mandé
5. Ya no la tengo.
   Se la di

B1. (Answers will vary.)

B2. (Answers will vary.)

EL RINCÓN CULTURAL

Una guía de salud
160 + 70 + 100 + 0 = 330
345 + 160 + 10 + 180 + 140 + 70 + 160 = 1.065
380 + 350 + 10 + 200 + 0 = 940

Nuestra dieta
(Answers will vary.)

VOCABULARY

1. a. orange
   b. sugar
   c. apricot
   d. alcohol
   e. saffron
   f. artichoke
2. g. algebra
   h. zero
   i. Gibraltar
   j. alkali
   k. alchemy
   l. zenith
3. m. admiral
   n. cotton
   o. jar
   p. checkmate
   q. crimson
   r. alfalfa
   s. cipher

TEST/REPASO ANSWERS

UNIDAD 1

(Answers)

TEST 1 La lotería

1.	100	5.	99
2.	15	6.	19
3.	30	7.	82
4.	74	8.	60

(Interpretation)

If you have made 2 or more mistakes, review the numbers on pages 16 and 18 of your textbook.

TEST 2 Antes y después

1. cinco, siete
2. ocho, diez
3. once, trece
4. catorce, diez y seis
5. diez y nueve, veinte y uno
6. domingo, martes
7. miércoles, viernes
8. enero, marzo
9. abril, junio
10. julio, septiembre
11. otoño, primavera
12. el cuatro de octubre, el seis de octubre
13. el primero de diciembre, el tres de diciembre

Items 1-2: If you have made any mistakes, review the numbers on page 16. Items 3-5: If you have made 2 or more mistakes, review the numbers on page 18. Items 6-10: If you have made 2 or more mistakes, review the days and months on page 28. Item 11: If you have made any mistakes, review the seasons on page 34. Items 12-13: If you have made any mistakes, review the dates on page 28.

TEST 3 En el aeropuerto

1. Es la una.
2. Son las tres y diez.
3. Son las cuatro y cuarto.
4. Son las cinco y media.
5. Son las siete menos cuarto.
6. Son las diez menos veinte.

Count ½ mistake for <u>every</u> wrong word. If you have 2 or more mistakes, review how to tell time on pages 21 and 24.

TEST 4 El mapa del tiempo

1.	llueve	4.	está nublado
2.	está nublado	5.	hace (mucho) calor (hace sol)
3.	hace viento	6.	nieva

If you have more than 1 incorrect <u>word</u>, review weather expressions on page 33.

TEST 5 Un encuentro

1. ¡Buenos días! (¡Hola!)
2. Me llamo . . .
3. Soy de . . .
4. Bien. (Muy bien, Así, así, Regular, Mal, Muy mal.)
5. ¡Hasta luego! (¡Hasta la vista!, ¡Adiós!)

Items 1-3: If you have any incorrect words, review the dialogs on pages 2 and 8. Items 4-5: If you have any incorrect words, review the greetings on pages 11 and 13.

TEST 6 Intérprete

1. ¿Qué hora es?
2. ¿Cuál es la fecha de hoy?
3. ¿Qué tiempo hace?
4. Por favor . . .
5. Muchas gracias.
6. De nada. (No hay de qué.)

If you have incorrect words, review the vocabulary on pages 21 and 25 (Item 1); page 28 (Item 2); page 33 (Item 3); and page 19 (Items 4-6).

TEST 7 ¿Sí o no?

sí: 2, 3, 4, 7, 8, 10, 11, 12
no: 1, 5, 6, 9

If you have 2 or more mistakes, reread the cultural notes of this unit.

UNIDAD 2

(Answers)

TEST 1 ¿Tenis?

1.	ella	5.	tú
2.	ellas	6.	usted (Ud.)
3.	ellos	7.	ustedes (Uds.)
4.	ellos	8.	ustedes (Uds.)

(Interpretation)

Items 1-4: If you made any mistakes, review Lección 2, Estructura A. Items 5-8: If you made any mistakes, review Lección 3, Estructura A, and Lección 4, Estructura A.

TEST 2   En San Carlos de Bariloche

1. Esquía	5. Esquías
2. Esquía	6. Esquía
3. Esquían	7. Esquío
4. Esquiamos	8. Esquiamos

If you made any mistakes, review Lección 4, Estructura B.

TEST 3   En la fiesta internacional

1. ¿Habla francés Enrique?
   no habla
2. ¿Hablan italiano Adela y Camila?
   hablan
3. ¿Hablas portugués?
   No hablo

If you made any mistakes in word order, review Lección 2, Estructura B. If you forgot the word **no,** review Lección 1, Estructura C.

TEST 4   Intérprete

1. ¡Tal vez!	6. No hablo español.
2. ¡Claro! (¡Por supuesto!, ¡Cómo no!)	7. No trabajo aquí.
	8. Me gusta viajar.
3. ¡Claro que no!	9. No me gusta hablar
4. No puedo.	francés.
5. ¡Qué lástima!	10. No deseo visitar París.

Items 1-5: If you made any mistakes, review the Entre nosotros sections. Items 6, 7, 9, 10: If you forgot the word **no,** review Lección 1, Estructura C. Items 8, 9: If you made any mistakes, review Lección 4, Estructura C. Item 10: If you made a mistake, review Lección 3, Estructura B.

TEST 5   La reciprocidad

1. Nosotros trabajamos para ti.
2. Ud. habla de él.
3. Uds. viajan con ella.
4. Él estudia conmigo.
5. Ellos visitan París contigo.

If you made any mistakes in the verb forms, review Lección 4, Estructura B. If you made any mistakes in the underlined pronouns, review Lección 4, Estructura D.

TEST 6   Actividades

1. trabaja	5. estudia
2. nada	6. escucha
3. mira	7. canta
4. toca	8. gana

If you made any mistakes, review the Vocabulario especializado on pages 52 and 59.

TEST 7   Una conversación

1. Cómo	4. Por qué
2. Dónde	5. Quién
3. Qué	6. Quiénes

If you made any mistakes, review the Vocabulario especializado on pages 66-67.

TEST 8   ¿Sí o no?

sí: 1, 2, 3, 9, 10, 13
no: 4, 5, 6, 7, 8, 11, 12

If you made 3 or more mistakes, review the Notas culturales.

UNIDAD 3

(Answers) *(Interpretation)*

TEST 1 En la aduana

1. somos, Venimos, Tenemos, franceses
2. eres, Vienes, Tienes, boliviano
3. soy, Vengo, Tengo, colombiano
4. son, Vienen, Tienen, dominicanos
5. son, Vienen, Tienen, italianos

If you made any mistakes with **ser,** review Estructura 1.C. If you made any mistakes with **venir,** review Estructura 4.B. If you made any mistakes with **tener,** review Estructura 3.A.

TEST 2 La orquesta de la escuela

1. El	4. Las
2. Los	5. Los
3. La	

If you made any mistakes, review Estructuras 1.A., 1.B., 3.B.

TEST 3 Las similitudes

1. unas, dinámicas	6. un, paciente
2. una, generosa	7. una, intelectual
3. unos, independientes	8. unas, populares
4. unas, sentimentales	9. unos, pesimistas
5. un, sincero	10. unos, generosos

Count one mistake for each word that contains an error. If you have three or more mistakes, review Estructuras 2.A., 3.B., 3.C.

TEST 4 El congreso estudiantil internacional

1. una estudiante española
2. un estudiante cubano
3. (unos) estudiantes mexicanos
4. (unas) estudiantes puertorriqueñas
5. (unos) estudiantes españoles
6. (unas) estudiantes españolas

If you put the adjective in the wrong position, review Estructura 2.B. If you made any mistakes on the forms of the adjectives, review the Vocabulario, page 112. If you made any mistakes on the forms of the indefinite article, review Estructuras 1.A. and 3.B.

TEST 5 Los nuevos alumnos
1. Tiene 16 años. Tiene 15 años.
2. Es rubia. Es moreno.
3. Es alta. Es bajo.
4. Es gorda. Es delgado.

Item 1: If you made a mistake, review Estructura 4.A. Items 2-4: If you made any mistakes, review the Vocabulario, page 93.

TEST 6 Los objetos perdidos
1. una bolsa
2. un televisor
3. un reloj
4. un disco
5. un libro
6. una revista
7. una bicicleta
8. un tocadiscos
9. un bolígrafo
10. una cinta

Count one mistake for each article and one mistake for each noun. If you have three or more mistakes, review the Vocabulario on pages 100-101.

TEST 7 Los opuestos se atraen
1. E
2. H
3. A
4. J
5. C
6. I
7. G
8. F
9. D

If you made any mistakes, review the Vocabulario on pages 93 and 101.

TEST 8 Intérprete
1. ¿Cuántos años tiene(s)?
2. ¿Tiene(s) que estudiar mucho?
3. ¿Tiene(s) que trabajar?
4. ¿Tiene(s) ganas de viajar?
5. ¿Cuántos libros tiene(s)?
6. ¿Cuántas cintas tiene(s)?
7. Hay un(a) profesor(a) mexicano(a).
    Hay un(a) maestro(a) mexicano(a).
8. Hay treinta estudiantes (alumnos).

Items 1-4: If you made any mistakes, review Estructura 4.A. Items 5-6: If you made any mistakes with **cuánto**, review the Vocabulario, page 106. Items 7-8: If you made any mistakes with **hay**, review the Vocabulario, pages 85 and 101.

TEST 9 ¿Sí o no?
sí: 2, 3, 4, 6
no: 1, 5, 7, 8

If you made 2 or more mistakes, reread the Notas culturales.

UNIDAD 4

(Answers)

(Interpretation)

TEST 1 De viaje
1. está, Va
2. estoy, Voy
3. está, Va
4. están, Van
5. estás, Vas
6. estamos, Vamos

Note the accent marks on certain forms of **estar**. If you made any mistakes with **estar**, review Estructura 2.A. If you made any mistakes with **ir**, review Estructura 2.B.

TEST 2 En el café
1. a
2. a
3. —
4. a
5. —

If you made any mistakes: review Estructura 1.A.

TEST 3 Un concurso de fotografía
1. a la de la
2. al del
3. a las de las

If you made any mistakes, review Estructura 1.B.

TEST 4 Descripciones
1. es, Es, está
2. es, está, está
3. es, está, Está
4. está, está, está
5. Está, está, Está
6. está, es, Es, es

If you made 2 or more mistakes, review Estructura 3.A.

TEST 5 Las vacaciones
1. . . . está nadando
2. . . . estamos nadando
3. . . . está hablando con Susana
4. . . . están sacando fotos
5. . . . está viajando
6. . . . estás mirando la televisión

If you made any mistakes, review Estructura 3.B.

TEST 6 De compras
1. los
2. no las
3. no lo
4. la
5. lo

If you made any mistakes in choice of pronoun or in word order, review Estructura 4.A.

TEST 7 El intruso
1. plaza
2. iglesia
3. triste
4. contento
5. nada
6. Tomo
7. llegar
8. tren

Items 1-2: If you made any mistakes, review the Vocabulario on page 142. Items 3-4: If you made any mistakes, review the Vocabulario on page 151. Items 5-7: If you made any mistakes, review the Vocabulario on pages 134-135. Item 8: If you made a mistake, review the Vocabulario on page 159. (Remember: Puerto Rico is an island.)

TEST 8 Intérprete
1. ¿Adónde vamos ahora?
2. ¿Dónde trabaja(s)?
3. ¿De dónde eres (es)?
4. ¿Va(s) a la playa?
5. ¿Está(s) en la playa?
6. Voy a casa.
7. Voy a (la) casa de Pedro.
8. Voy a nadar. ¿Y tú (Ud.)?
9. ¿Va(s) a nadar con nosotros?
10. Pedro va a sacar fotos.
11. ¿Cuándo va(s) a visitar Madrid?

TEST 9 ¿Sí o no?
sí: 2, 3, 4, 6, 7
no: 1, 5, 8, 9, 10

If you made any mistakes with the underlined words, review the Vocabulario on page 145. If you made any mistakes with the construction **ir a** + infinitive, review Estructura 2.C.

If you made more than 2 mistakes, reread the Notas culturales.

UNIDAD 5

(Answers)

TEST 1 En la biblioteca

1.	lee escribo	4.	lees escribe
2.	leen escribe	5.	leo escribo
3.	lee escribimos	6.	leemos escribes

(Interpretation)

If you made any mistakes, review Estructura 1.A.

TEST 2 De venta

1.	mis	5.	tu	9.	su
2.	su	6.	nuestra	10.	sus
3.	su	7.	su		
4.	nuestros	8.	sus		

If you made two or more mistakes, review Estructura 4.A.

TEST 3 Actividades

A. 1. hago
    2. hacen
    3. hace
    4. hacemos
    5. haces

B. 1. digo
    2. dice
    3. dicen
    4. decimos
    5. dices

C. 1. da
    2. doy
    3. da
    4. dan
    5. das

Section A: If you made any mistakes, review Estructura 2.C. Section B: If you made any mistakes, review Estructura 3.A. Section C: If you made any mistakes, review Estructura 4.C.

TEST 4 La amiga ideal

1.	Lo	5.	Le	9.	La
2.	Le	6.	Les	10.	Las
3.	Lo	7.	Los		
4.	Le	8.	Le		

If you made 2 or more mistakes, review Estructuras 4.B. and 4.D.

TEST 5 Intérprete
1. ¿Dónde está la guitarra de Pedro?
2. ¿Dónde está el hermano de Carmen?
3. ¿Dónde están los (las) amigos(as) del Sr. Ortega?
4. ¿Cuándo (A qué hora) es la clase de español?
5. ¿Quién es el (la) profesor(a) de música?
6. ¿Tienes discos de jazz?

Items 1-3: If you made any mistakes, review Estructura 1.C. Items 4-6: If you made any mistakes with the underlined constructions, review Estructura 2.B.

TEST 6 El intruso

1.	cree	5.	cree	9.	ayudo
2.	vende	6.	come	10.	buscas
3.	asiste	7.	bebo	11.	compra
4.	come	8.	Vives	12.	ayudar

Items 1-8: If you made any mistakes, review the Vocabulario, pages 170-171. Items 9-12: If you made any mistakes, review the Vocabulario, pages 196 and 198.

TEST 7 La familia

1.	abuelo	4.	primas
2.	abuela	5.	hermanos
3.	tío		

If you made any mistakes, review the Vocabulario on page 179.

TEST 8 La arquitectura

1.	el árbol	4.	el comedor	7.	la ventana
2.	el garaje	5.	la cocina	8.	la sala
3.	la puerta	6.	el cuarto	9.	el baño

Count one mistake for each wrong noun and one mistake for each wrong article. If you have 3 or more mistakes, review the Vocabulario on page 190.

TEST 9 El orden cronológico

1. primer
2. primeros
3. segundo
4. tercer
5. décimo
6. séptimo

TEST 10 ¿Sí o no?

sí: 2, 3, 5, 7, 8
no: 1, 4, 6

If you made any mistakes, review the Vocabulario, page 187.

If you made any mistakes, reread the Notas culturales.

UNIDAD 6

(Answers)

(Interpretation)

TEST 1 Diálogos

A. Te
B. Te Me
C. nos_ las
D. Me Lo

If you made any mistakes, review Estructura 1.A.

TEST 2 Expresión personal

1. La televisión norteamericana (no) es interesante.
2. La música norteamericana (no) es muy buena.
3. El fútbol norteamericano (no) es violento.
4. Los chicos norteamericanos (no) son inteligentes.
5. Las chicas norteamericanas (no) son deportistas.
6. Las escuelas norteamericanas (no) son buenas.

If you left out the definite article, review Estructura 2.B.

TEST 3 La crítica

1. el
2. me gustan los
3. gustan
4. me gusta la
5. Te gustan las
6. no me gusta el

Count one mistake for every wrong word. If you made more than 2 mistakes, review Estructuras 2.B. and 2.C.

TEST 4 El sarampión

1. no nada
2. No nadie
3. No nada
4. Nadie
5. no ningún

Count one mistake for every wrong word. If you made two or more mistakes, review Estructura 1.B.

TEST 5 El fin de semana

A.
1. juego
2. juegan
3. jugamos
4. juegas

B.
1. pido
2. pide
3. piden
4. pedimos

C.
1. encuentro
2. encuentra
3. encontramos
4. encuentras

D.
1. quiero
2. quieren
3. queremos
4. quieres

E.
1. duermo
2. duerme
3. duermen
4. dormimos
5. duermes

Section A: If you made any mistakes, review Estructura 2.A. Section B: If you made any mistakes, review Estructura 1.C. Section C: If you made any mistakes, review Estructura 3.C. Section D: If you made any mistakes, review Estructura 3.B. Section E: If you made any mistakes, review Estructura 3.C.

TEST 6 Conversación

1. conozco
2. Salgo
3. pongo
4. conduzco

If you made any mistakes, review Estructuras 4.B. and 4.C.

TEST 7 Intérprete

1. No voy nunca al teatro. (Nunca voy al teatro.)
2. No escucho nunca la radio. (Nunca escucho la radio.)
3. ¿Qué hace(s) los domingos?
4. ¿Trabaja(s) los sábados?
5. El lunes, voy a invitar a Carlos.
6. El martes, voy a llamar a Silvia.

Items 1-2: If you made any mistakes with the underlined words, review Estructura 1.B. Items 3-6: If you made any mistakes with the underlined words, review the Vocabulario, page 244.

TEST 8 La palabra exacta

1. gasto
2. pagar
3. pide
4. pregunto
5. La natación
6. equipo
7. Pienso
8. empieza
9. Quieres
10. cuesta
11. perder
12. duermo
13. puedo
14. obedece
15. trae

Items 1-2: If you made any mistakes, review the Vocabulario, pages 218-219. Items 3-4: If you made any mistakes, review Estructura 1.C, note. Items 5-6: If you made any mistakes, review the Vocabulario, page 226. Items 7-13: If you made any mistakes, review the Vocabulario, pages 236 and 239, and Estructura 3.B. Items 14-15: If you made any mistakes, review Estructuras 4.B and 4.C.

TEST 9 ¿Sí o no?

sí: 3, 6, 8, 10
no: 1, 2, 4, 5, 7, 9, 11, 12

If you made 2 or more mistakes, reread the Notas culturales.

UNIDAD 7

TEST 1 Las comparaciones

1. más que
2. menos que
3. tan como
4. el más
5. el más

Count one mistake for each incorrect word. If you have 2 or more mistakes, review Estructuras 1.B. and 1.C.

TEST 2 En el almacén grande

1. este 2. estos 3. esta 4. esas 5. ese 6. Esos 7. aquel
8. aquella 9. Aquellas

If you have 2 or more mistakes, review Estructura 2.A.

TEST 3 El lanzamiento en paracaídas

1. se prepara
2. me preparo
3. se prepara
4. se preparan
5. nos preparamos
6. te preparas

If you made any mistakes in the reflexive pronouns, review Estructura 3.A.

TEST 4 Actividades

1. Se
2. Lo
3. Lo
4. Se
5. lo
6. se
7. se
8. La

If you made any mistakes, review Estructura 3.A.

TEST 5 El fin de semana

1. van a quedarse
2. voy a quedarme
3. Vas a quedarte
4. vamos a quedarnos
5. va a quedarse

Count one mistake for each wrong pronoun or for each error in word order. If you made any mistakes, review Estructura 4.C.

TEST 6 Intérprete

1. ¿Prefieres (Te gusta más) el coche azul o el rojo?
2. Me gusta la casa grande pero prefiero (me gusta más) la pequeña.
3. Tengo el pelo negro.
4. Elena tiene los ojos azules.
5. Carlos se lava las manos.
6. Josefina se lava el pelo.

Items 1-2: If you made any mistakes with the underlined expressions, review Estructura 2.B. Items 3-6: If you made any mistakes with the underlined expressions, review Estructura 4.A.

TEST 7 Un poco de anatomía

1. la mano
2. el brazo
3. el pie
4. la cara
5. la nariz
6. la boca
7. el ojo
8. la oreja
9. la espalda
10. la pierna

Count one mistake for each wrong noun and one mistake for each wrong article. If you made more than 3 mistakes, review the Vocabularios on pages 257 and 284.

TEST 8 Los sospechosos

A. 1. sombrero 2. abrigo 3. pantalones
B. 4. anteojos 5. vestido 6. zapatos
C. 7. blusa 8. falda 9. calcetines
D. 10. camisa 11. corbata 12. traje

If you made 2 or more mistakes, review the Vocabulario on page 266.

TEST 9 El verbo que conviene

1. Me lavo
2. peinarse
3. se pone
4. se viste
5. bañarse
6. quedarme
7. sentirte
8. se sienta
9. levantarme
10. me acuesto

Items 1-5: If you made any mistakes, review the Vocabulario on pages 278-279. Items 6-10: If you made any mistakes, review the Vocabulario on page 286.

TEST 10 ¿Sí o no?

sí: 1, 3, 4, 5, 8, 9
no: 2, 6, 7, 10

If you made 2 or more mistakes, reread the Notas culturales.

UNIDAD 8

TEST 1 En la fiesta

1. bailó
2. bailaron
3. bailamos
4. bailé
5. bailaste
6. bailó
7. bailaron
8. bailamos

If you made 2 or more mistakes, review Estructura 2.A.

TEST 2 Ayer y hoy

1. Hablaste
2. Trabajamos
3. Tocaron
4. Invité
5. Comí
6. Recibí
7. Comiste
8. escribiste
9. Rompió
10. comprendió
11. Bebimos
12. Recibimos
13. Vendieron
14. Recibieron

Items 1-4: If you made any mistakes, review Estructura 2.A. Items 5-14: If you made any mistakes, review Estructura 3.A.

TEST 3 Raúl y Ramón

1. toqué
2. saqué
3. llegué
4. organicé
5. encontré
6. pensé
7. sentí
8. empecé
9. jugué
10. vi
11. di

Items 1-4: If you made any mistakes, review Estructura 2.B. Items 5-6: If you made any mistakes, review Estructura 4.A. Item 7: If you made a mistake, review Estructura 4.B. Items 8-9: If you made any mistakes, review Estructuras 2.B. and 4.A. Items 10-11: If you made any mistakes, review Estructura 3.B.

TEST 4 Intérprete

1. Acabo de hablar con Ana.
2. Emilio acaba de ir al cine.
3. Acabamos de ver a Enrique.
4. Hace un año que vivo en San Juan.
5. Hace un mes que Clara trabaja aquí.
6. Hace seis meses que estudiamos español.

Items 1-3: If you made any mistakes with the underlined expressions, review Estructura 1.A. Items 4-6: If you made any mistakes with the underlined expressions, review Estructura 1.B.

TEST 5 En el restaurante

1. agua
2. hamburguesa
3. helado
4. cerveza
5. gaseosa

If you made any mistakes, review the Vocabulario, page 332.

TEST 6 La lógica

1. nota
2. útil
3. equivoco
4. dejar
5. pasar
6. Me olvidé
7. esta noche
8. Ayer
9. temprano
10. descubrió
11. debe
12. me rompí
13. sueño
14. sed

Items 1-2: If you made any mistakes, review the Vocabulario, page 310. Items 3-9: If you made any mistakes, review the Vocabulario, page 318. Items 10-12: If you made any mistakes, review the Vocabulario, page 324. Items 13-14: If you made any mistakes, review the Vocabulario, page 332.

TEST 7 ¿Sí o no?

sí: 2, 4, 7, 8, 9, 11, 12
no: 1, 3, 5, 6, 10

If you made 2 or more mistakes, reread the Notas culturales.

UNIDAD 9

(Answers)

(Interpretation)

TEST 1 En el club deportivo

1. a
2. —
3. de
4. a
5. de
6. a
7. a
8. —

If you made 2 or more mistakes, review Estructura 2.A.

TEST 2 El fin de semana pasado

1. fuimos
2. fue
3. fuiste
4. fue
5. fui
6. fueron
7. fueron
8. fue

If you made any mistakes, review Estructura 3.A.

TEST 3 Lo que me gusta

1. conduje
2. Traje
3. dije
4. Hice
5. Estuve
6. Puse
7. Supe
8. Pude

Items 1-3: If you made any mistakes, review Estructura 3.B. Items 4-8: If you made any mistakes, review Estructura 4.A.

TEST 4 La estación de tren en Madrid

1. para
2. por
3. por
4. para
5. para
6. por
7. por
8. por
9. para
10. para
11. por
12. para

If you made 2 or more mistakes, review Estructuras 2.C. and 3.C.

TEST 5 Preguntas

1. Conoces
2. Sabes
3. Conoces
4. Sabes
5. Conoces
6. Conoces
7. Sabes
8. Sabes
9. Conoces
10. Sabes

If you made 2 or more mistakes, review Estructura 1.A.

TEST 6 Intérprete

1. Trabajo para ganar dinero.
2. ¿Estudia(s) español para ir a España?
3. Antes de ir a París, quiero aprender francés.
4. Voy a visitar México después de visitar Guatemala.
5. No comprendo lo que dice(s).
6. ¿Cree(s) lo que digo?
7. Voy al cine de vez en cuando.
8. El mes pasado, fui al cine dos veces.
9. ¿Cuántas veces fuiste (fue) al cine?

Items 1-4: If you made any mistakes with the underlined expressions, review Estructura 2.B. Items 5-6: If you made any mistakes with the underlined words, review Estructura 4.B. Items 7-9: If you made any mistakes with the underlined expressions, review the Vocabulario on page 367.

TEST 7 Un trabajo para cada uno

1. M	4. H	7. E	10. F
2. J	5. L	8. K	11. C
3. I	6. A	9. G	12. B

If you made 2 or more mistakes, review the Vocabulario, pages 343, 355 and 378.

TEST 8 ¿Sí o no?

sí: 1, 2, 3, 6, 9

no: 4, 5, 7, 8, 10

If you made 2 or more mistakes, reread the Notas culturales.

UNIDAD 10

(Answers)

(Interpretation)

TEST 1 Las relaciones de Carlos

1. la	4. Los	7. Le	10. Los
2. Le	5. La	8. Te	11. Les
3. les	6. me	9. Le	12. nos

If you made more than 2 mistakes, review Estructura 1.A.

TEST 2 Sí y no

1. Compra 2. compres
3. Piensa 4. pienses
5. Aprende 6. aprendas
7. Vuelve 8. vuelvas
9. Juega 10. juegues
11. Escribe 12. escribas

If you made any mistakes in the odd-numbered items, review Estructura 1.B. If you made any mistakes in the even-numbered items, review Estructura 2.A.

TEST 3 Unos consejos

1. Pon	4. Di	7. Sé
2. Sal	5. Ten	8. Ven
3. Ve	6. Haz	

If you made 2 or more mistakes, review Estructuras 3.A. and 3.B.

TEST 4 De prisa

1. Llámame 4. los rompas
2. invítala 5. Quédate
3. le prestes 6. te acuestes

If you made any mistakes in the position of the underlined pronouns, review Estructuras 1.C. and 2.B.

TEST 5 Intérprete

1. Compra el disco y préstamelo.
2. Compra las revistas y mándamelas.
3. Compra el libro pero no me lo mandes.
4. Compra los periódicos pero no me los mandes.

If you made any mistakes with the position of the underlined pronouns, review Estructura 3.C.

TEST 6 Un hijo servicial

sí: 2, 4, 7, 8, 9, 10, 14, 16, 17, 18

no: 1, 3, 5, 6, 11, 12, 13, 15

If you made 2 or more mistakes, review the Vocabulario on pages 402 and 406-407.

TEST 7 La carrera

1. detrás 4. hacia
2. lejos 5. al lado
3. izquierda 6. delante

If you made any mistakes, review the Vocabulario on page 426.

TEST 8 ¿Sí o no?

sí: 1, 2, 3, 4, 6, 7, 10

no: 5, 8, 9

If you made 2 or more mistakes, reread the Notas culturales.